KU-662-292

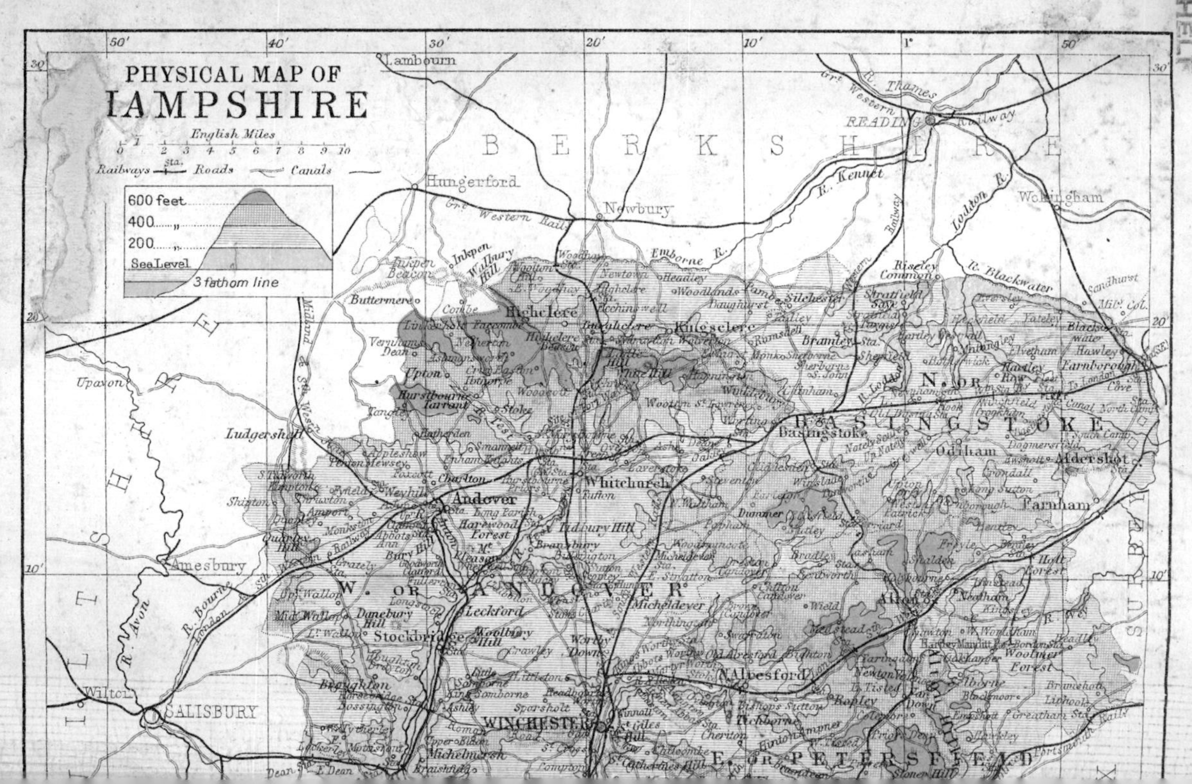
PHYSICAL MAP OF
IAMPSHIRE
English Miles
Railways Sta. Roads Canals
600 feet
400 „
200 „
Sea Level
3 fathom line
BERKSHIRE
SURREY
WILTSHIRE
READING
R. Thames
Gr.t Western Railway
R. Kennet
Newbury
Hungerford
Lambourn
Wokingham
R. Blackwater
Loddon R.
Emborne R.
Sandhurst
Highclere
Kingsclere
Silchester
Basingstoke
N. OR BASINGSTOKE
Odiham
Aldershot
Farnham
Farnborough
Whitchurch
Andover
W. OR ANDOVER
Ludgershall
Amesbury
Upavon
SALISBURY
Wilton
R. Avon
R. Bourne
Stockbridge
Leckford
Danebury Hill
Micheldever
Alresford
Alton
Woolmer Forest
WINCHESTER
E. OR PETERSFIELD
Tichborne
Cheriton
Ropley
Inkpen Beacon
Walbury Hill
Buttermere
Tidbury Hill
Woolbury Hill
Quarley Hill
Michelmersh
Broughton
Newton Valence
Dummer

The Cambridge University Press

CAMBRIDGE COUNTY GEOGRAPHIES

General Editor: F. H. H. Guillemard, M.A., M.D.

HAMPSHIRE

CAMBRIDGE UNIVERSITY PRESS

C. F. CLAY, MANAGER

LONDON : FETTER LANE, E.C.4

NEW YORK : THE MACMILLAN CO.
BOMBAY }
CALCUTTA } MACMILLAN AND CO., LTD.
MADRAS }
TORONTO : THE MACMILLAN CO. OF CANADA, LTD.
TOKYO : MARUZEN-KABUSHIKI-KAISHA

Cambridge County Geographies

HAMPSHIRE

By

TELFORD VARLEY

Head Master, Peter Symonds' School, Winchester

With Maps, Diagrams, and Illustrations

CAMBRIDGE

AT THE UNIVERSITY PRESS

1922

Printed in Scotland
by Turnbull & Spears, Edinburgh

PREFACE

The author begs to express his cordial thanks to many friends who have given him valuable assistance in connection with the following pages—to Canon J. Vaughan, for kindly reading the proof sheets dealing with the flora of the county, and for information relating thereto; to Mr H. W. Butler, Assistant County Surveyor, for information as to roads and other topics; to Mr H. J. Farmer, Borough Surveyor of Christchurch, for information as to coastal changes at the harbour mouth; to Dr Williams Freeman for varied information; to Mr J. C. Newsham, formerly of the County Farm Institute; and to many others. The author wishes also to acknowledge the valuable help received by him from Mr Clement Hopkins, of Isleworth School.

The maps on pp. 39 and 68 (published in the Geological Survey *Memoirs*) are inserted by permission of the Controller of His Majesty's Stationery Office. The details of the geological section on p. 36 are taken, by permission, from a section published by Messrs Ed. Stanford Ltd., Long Acre.

TELFORD VARLEY

Winchester, 1921

CONTENTS

ILLUSTRATIONS

MAPS

The illustrations on pp. 7, 18, 57, 120, 125, 129, 144, 145, 195, 198, 205 are reproduced from photographs by Messrs J. Valentine & Sons, Ltd.; those on pp. 13, 15, 16, 20, 25, 29, 45, 47, 48, 49, 91, 93, 94, 97, 109, 152, 153, 154, 162, 182, 189 from photographs specially taken by the author; that on p. 99 is included by courtesy of the Topical Press Assoc.; that on p. 103 is reproduced from a photograph kindly supplied by Mr R. Urie, of the L. & S.W. Railway Engineering Department, Eastleigh; that on p. 116 is from a photograph by Mr Stuart, kindly supplied by the White Star Line; those on pp. 123, 139, 141, 142, 147, 168, 187, 206, 207 are from photographs by Messrs F. Frith & Co., Ltd.; that on p. 138 from a photograph by the Rev. G. Sampson; that on p. 176 is reproduced from a photograph by Emery Walker, Ltd.; that on p. 177 by arrangement with the Royal Society for the Prevention of Cruelty to Animals; and that on p. 180 by kind permission of the Dean and Chapter of St Paul's Cathedral.

1. County and Shire

England is divided into areas curiously dissimilar in size and shape, known as "shires" or "counties"—a division of much interest historically, for it carries us back to the days of the Anglo-Saxon occupation.

On the decay of Roman civilisation and the withdrawal of their legions from Britain about A.D. 420, successive waves of barbarism swept over the country, Pictish tribes from the north, Scots from Ireland, and Jutes, Angles, and Saxons from over sea. In this deluge most of what was Roman was swept away, and for some 350 years these tribes occupied the land, warring one with another, and gradually establishing kingdoms—the so-called Heptarchy. It was at this early period, before England had become welded into one nation, that we got the word "shire," which is derived from the Anglo-Saxon "scire"—a *share,* that is, or division of land *shorn off* from a larger portion. As the Anglo-Saxons spread over the country, the land became increasingly covered with small settlements, or village communities, till ultimately the whole area was carved out into a number of separate estates or properties, known for the most part as "tuns," "worths," or "hams." The members of each community cultivated the soil in common, under a lord or owner, but had clearly defined rights of their own. These varied from "tun" to "tun," and the various "tuns," with their lords or owners, were independent one of another, except in so far as common action was necessary for mutual protection. As the kingdoms developed, however, they became more and more organised, and in comparatively early Heptarchy days each had come to be divided into portions known as *scires*—the originals of our "shires"—of the present day. Each *scire* was governed by an *Ealdorman*, and an administrative officer, the *scire-gerefa*, *i.e.* "shire-reeve" (our modern offices of Alderman and Sheriff), while for minor purposes of government the "tunships" were grouped together into districts called "hundreds."

Each unit in this triple series of shire, hundred, and tunship had its own administrative assembly, known as the *moot* or meeting, at which matters affecting their general welfare were discussed and determined. All subsequent developments of local government have practically grown from this. Thus from the early tun grew the *demesne* or *manor* of later Anglo-Saxon and Norman days, with the parish as its ecclesiastical equivalent.

The later word county is derived from the Norman title of *comte* or count, the *comes* (companion) of the king, and the county is therefore the *comitatus* or "countship," *i.e.* the area governed by a count. Thus, while the words shire and county both stand for the same thing, their origins are widely different. One tells us of development of local institution going back to early Anglo-Saxon times, the other, of the subjugation of the Saxon to the Norman invader.

The name of our county is recorded for the first time in history in the English *Chronicle*, under date A.D. 755, where we read that "Sigeberht, King of Wessex, was deprived by the Witan of all his possessions except Heantunscire." This name connects it with the great seaport on its coast, Southampton, known in earlier days as Hantune, and in medieval times as Hampton. Later, when to avoid confusion with the midland town, the prefix "Suth" *i.e.* "south," was added, the seaport became Suth hantune, and the county "Suthhantunscire." Thus while in ordinary parlance we speak of Hampshire, the true style of our county is the "County of Southampton," and as such it appears in all legal and official documents, both present and past.

As to the derivation of the word "Hantune," more than one explanation has been given. The usual and apparently obvious one is that Hantune (or Hampton) means the Home-town, the headquarters or principal town of the original Anglo-Saxon settlers, the Gewissas. Others, again, in view of the fact that the Test River is known as the Anton above Fullerton Junction, and probably in early times all down its course as far as the Solent, have explained Hantune as being connected with the name Clausentum (the Roman Southampton), both Hantune and Clausentum being thus derived from "an," a Celtic word meaning water, which occurs elsewhere in many other of our county place-names. Whatever the explanation may be, the name of the county is undoubtedly of the same origin as that of the seaport, which in early days, as at the present time, has so greatly influenced its fortunes.

It is important to note that different meanings are attached to the word county. When we mean the whole geographical area, corresponding practically to the original Hantunscire, we term it the "Ancient County." It is in this sense that Hampshire is used when we speak of "the Lord Lieutenant of Hampshire," or "the population of Hampshire" as given in the Census Reports, and it is in this sense (excluding the Isle of Wight, which is dealt with in a separate volume) that we shall ordinarily use the term. But for certain purposes of local administration, administration of justice, and Parliamentary election, municipal boroughs have for many years had powers of self-government, and while included in the county area for some purposes, are independent areas for others. In 1888 the larger municipal boroughs, Portsmouth and Southampton, and later Bournemouth, were given the status, for administrative purposes, of separate counties, under the name of County Boroughs, while the remainder was divided into two "Administrative Counties," the mainland forming the "Administrative County of Southampton," and the Isle of Wight becoming a separate administrative county, each under a County Council.

2. General Characteristics

Hampshire may be roughly described as a maritime county with peculiar coastal features and comprising a number of distinct areas differing markedly one from the other. It is almost purely agricultural. There are few large centres of population and very few manufactures. The industries followed are mostly those dictated by local needs. The climate is warm and genial, the scenery almost everywhere attractive, and there is consequently a large and rapidly increasing residential population.

Perhaps the most marked feature of rural Hampshire is its extensive woodland area, which is greater than that of any other English county. In ancient times a huge belt of forest covered nearly all the south-eastern and southern districts of England. Of this—the ancient forest of Anderida—practically no portion survives locally except perhaps the wild tangle of wood known as Harting Combe, just beyond the eastern border, and possibly some parts of the New Forest in the west of the county, but the same climatic conditions which favoured the growth of timber trees in early days still prevail, and timber is found over large areas.

The next striking feature is the large extent of waste and uncultivated land—chalk upland or sandy heath—the chalk downs in the centre and north covered with fine turf, the sandy heaths along the north-east, east, and south-west, covered with furze and heather; so that wild life has suffered less in Hampshire than in almost any other English county, and there is an unusually extensive flora and fauna. Over the wide rolling downs sheep-rearing has been carried on for centuries; indeed in medieval days the wool industry was the staple industry, and Hampshire wool was a leading item in the commerce of the land. In particular areas special cultivations, such as hops and strawberries, are now extensively carried on but, in the main, general farming and the ordinary minor industries connected with it form the chief occupations of the inland population.

Another outstanding feature of Hampshire is the almost entire absence of mineral wealth. There are no mines, no coal, and very little building stone. Brick-earth exists plentifully and bricks can be made almost everywhere, but this is practically all. Hence the almost exclusively rural character of inland Hampshire.

The sea-board has special features of its own. All along the coast are well-marked river estuaries and land-locked harbours, and lying athwart them all is the Isle of Wight, which acts as a protection to Spithead, Southampton Water, and the Solent behind it. These sheltered waterways give ready access to the ocean east and west, and tidal conditions are such as always to afford a good depth of water. Southampton indeed possesses unusually favourable conditions for commerce, not merely from its geographical position, and the security of its waterways, but also from its "hinterland." It is practically as near to London as Harwich or Dover, and railways connect it directly with the great

Mark Ash, New Forest

(*Showing characteristic forest beech growth, here seen at its best*)

coal-producing and manufacturing districts of the Midlands and South Wales. Natural conditions thus seem to mark it out as the future colonial distributing port of England.

It is to the same conditions, viz. central position, ease of access to the ocean and the "hinterland," and security from weather and from foreign attack, that Portsmouth owes its position as the greatest naval port and arsenal in the world. Ever since Roman days Portsmouth Harbour has been a naval centre, and it is now by far the largest urban area of the county. Its industries—which are those naturally arising in a great naval and victualling port—support something like one-third of the whole population of the county.

The sheltered character of the Hampshire inland waters, the beauty of its coastal scenery and that of the Isle of Wight, and the excellence of the climate, render the neighbourhood especially attractive for yachting, and all through the summer months Hampshire coastal waters abound with every type of pleasure craft.

Comparing the inland and the maritime features of the county we see that it is the latter and not the inland characters to which it owes its chief importance. Nevertheless rural Hampshire is essentially the producing part, the seaports merely the distributing.

3. Size. Shape. Boundaries

The "Ancient County" of Hampshire has a total area of 1,053,042 acres, of which 94,146 are in the Isle of

Wight, the remainder, 958,896 acres, forming the mainland area which we are studying. Of this some 4000 acres are water.

Compared with others, Hampshire is a large county. In point of size it stands seventh on the list, being exceeded only by Yorkshire, Lincolnshire, Devon, Norfolk, Northumberland and Lancashire, in the order given.

Roughly speaking, the Hampshire mainland forms a sort of square, measuring some 40 miles from north to south, and from east to west. The greatest distance from boundary to boundary is from Bournemouth in the south-west corner to Farnborough in the north-east, a distance of about 67 miles. The county boundaries are largely natural. The same considerations which dictated the limits of the "tunships" or manors of earlier days, were likewise operative in determining those of the county. These were mainly, though not entirely, geographical, though as time went on various alterations would naturally ensue owing to sale and purchase of property and other like causes, all of which have had their influence in shaping the Hampshire of to-day.

Starting from the coast at the western extremity, the boundary runs from a point about six miles from the mouth of Christchurch Harbour (now the western limit of the quite modern town of Bournemouth), and proceeds northward, following roughly the line of the watershed of the Avon valley, keeping at a distance of about three miles from the stream, to a point near Fordingbridge. Here the Avon is joined by the little tributary stream, the Allen, whose valley the county boundary practically outlines in exactly the same way, till reaching the head of the Allen valley it turns sharply eastward, crosses the Avon directly at right angles a little north of Breamore, and then keeps along the edge of the well-defined escarpment which connects North Charford and Bramshaw "Telegraph." It now turns northward, and meeting the valley of the Test, outlines it in much the same manner, running parallel first to the main stream and afterwards to its tributary, the Wallop Brook, till near Shipton Bellinger it meets the valley of the Wiltshire river, the Bourne. Crossing the Bourne, it outlines its valley as far as Tidworth, and then, turning sharply to the east, and crossing it again, keeps an easterly course till it reaches a point two miles south of Tangley. Here the surface is very broken, and the elevation high, averaging some 600 feet above sea level, and the boundary follows in the main the ridges of the higher ground, and except at one spot, viz. Combe, where an important alteration was made a few years ago, follows this natural line as far as Pilot Hill (874 feet high). At this point it turns sharply and descends into the Enborne valley as far as the river, which now forms the boundary for a distance of almost seven miles. Leaving the river, it follows another natural line marked out for it by the old Roman road between Speen and Silchester, and passing northwards by an irregular bend round Silchester itself, again follows the Roman road from Southampton to London for some six miles, till it meets the Blackwater, which it follows as far as its source near Aldershot, a distance of some sixteen miles, and then takes a more or less winding course southward, either skirting the streams and outlining their valleys, or in the more elevated areas keeping the line of the ridges, till between Grayshott and Hindhead it rises to something like 700 feet. Keeping the same general character, it passes through Rake and close to Sheet, crosses directly over the Rother valley two miles east of Petersfield, and then passing across the line of the South Downs by a fairly well-defined gap between Buriton and Harting, it holds a direct course till it meets the coast at Emsworth, at the head of Chichester Harbour. From this point onward, the boundary is a water boundary, following the centre of the tideway, until it meets the open sea, a little east of Hayling Island.

A few years ago the outline of the county in one or two localities was much more complicated and, for the reasons indicated above, parish boundaries and county boundaries did not always coincide, and this gave rise to many inconveniences. By the provisions of the Local Government Act of 1894, however, the whole of every parish and, unless the County Council otherwise directed, the whole of each rural district, were placed within the same administrative area. In Hampshire this Act caused the following changes:—the ancient parish of Combe in the north-west was transferred to Berkshire, and the modern parish of Dockenfield in the middle east to Surrey; part of Bramshott parish was transferred from Sussex to Hampshire, and the Wiltshire parishes of Bramshaw East, Damerham,

Martin, Melchet, Plaitford, Toyd Farm with Allenford, West Wellow, and part of Whitsbury were handed over to Hampshire. The main result was to straighten out the more irregular portions of the county boundary, though in the case of Combe, to which we have already referred, it was carried out in defiance of all natural geographical conditions. Combe, as its name implies, lies in an extremely deep hollow, and the county boundary, which formerly took the natural geographical line along the ridge of the steep escarpment to the north of it, now descends abruptly into the valley below, and then reascends the hill slope some miles further west.

4. Surface and General Features

We cannot too clearly realise that the varied phenomena which it is the function of geography to investigate are either immediately or ultimately the outcome of certain natural causes, chief among which are (1) geographical position; (2) elevation; (3) the nature of the soil or rock, and (4) climate; and all of these, while they mutually interact, are largely brought about by one central physical cause—geological structure. We shall therefore proceed to enquire how this has affected our county.

The foundation, or base as it were, of Hampshire is the chalk, which forms the core of the county and stretches as an elevated plateau over the whole of the centre, flanked on its northern, eastern, and southern slopes by a series of sands, clays, and gravels, and dividing the county into five distinct areas, each marked by well-defined characteristics. These areas are :—

(i.) The central Chalk Upland or central plateau.

(ii.) The area of clays and sands lying to the north-east and sloping to the Thames. This is known as the "Woodlands."

St Catherine's Hill, near Winchester

(*A neolithic "Ring" surmounts the hill*)

(iii.) The narrow maritime belt of clays and sands, east of Southampton Water, between the upland and the sea, which we may term the Coastal Fringe.

(iv.) The area of sands and gravels west of Southampton Water, between the chalk upland and the sea, a well-defined area known as the New Forest.

(v.) The region east of the central chalk upland. This is really the western extremity of the Weald, which here protrudes into Hampshire from Sussex, and which for want of a better name we may call the Selborne area.

The surface of the Chalk Plateau, though as a rule elevated, is by no means level, but presents the characteristic series of rolling ridge and hollow which distinguishes this formation. In many places this chalk forms practically the actual surface, with merely a few inches of soil on the top. Where this is the case we get the beautiful down country, with wide stretches of turf, over which the eye can range uninterruptedly for many miles. More generally, however, the chalk is overlaid with clayey or loamy soil, possibly a good many feet in depth, and here farms prevail. This is almost invariably the case in the hollows and lower levels all through the chalk upland, for the latter was once completely covered many feet thick with clayey material, and though nearly all of it has since been worn or washed away, it has naturally collected or persisted longer in the hollows, and it is still continually accumulating there. Thus, while on portions of the upper slopes or ridges we shall find nothing growing but the natural vegetation of the chalk land, namely turf and juniper, in other places where a thin layer of soil exists we shall find yew and beech; but only in the hollows where there is a deep soil shall we meet with elm or ash, hawthorn or sycamore, and if oak or holly are present we shall know that underneath there is probably a good depth of strong marly loam or heavy clay.

Another interesting and instructive point to note

Beacon Hill, near Burghclere

(*Showing open chalk slopes, covered with juniper, and ancient cultivation terraces at the base*)

is the variation of soil as we approach the limit of cultivation in a chalk valley. The gently curving character of the summits of the chalk downs is typical of them, but as the hills descend they often take a steeper slope, occasionally forming well-defined or even bold escarpments, and sometimes they meet the

Shawford Valley
(*Showing natural hedge along the cultivation limit*)

soil wash lying in the bed of the valley at quite a sharp angle. Where this is the case the limit of cultivation almost always occurs at the angle, but whatever course the limit takes, it usually indicates a definite degree of soil thickness.

The chalk upland reaches its greatest elevation along two or more well-marked ridges, the chief of which are the North Downs and the South Downs. The former stretch across the county from the Wiltshire downland in the north-west corner in a curve, first eastward and then southward, with a general level of from 750 to 870 feet above the sea, the chief elevations being Beacon Hill (858 feet), Ladle Hill (768 feet), Pilot Hill (874 feet), and King John's Hill (754 feet), after which they broaden out at Medstead into a plateau of some 700 feet elevation, and then curve southward forming steep escarpments again facing eastward at Noar Hill (696 feet), Wheatham Hill (813 feet) and Stonor Hill (756 feet).

The line of the South Downs, though less continuous, is more direct. On the west it reaches a general elevation of 500 feet, but eastward it rises higher to Beacon Hill and Old Winchester Hill (each about 660 feet), and Butser Hill, the highest point in the county (889 feet). All round Butser Hill the county is wonderfully picturesque, with deep combes and valleys, often really bold in contour.

This chalk upland is not continuous, but is intersected at various points by river valleys, which have cleft deep fissures in it, the course and causes of which we shall presently examine. The bottoms and lower levels of these valleys are filled with rich alluvial soil, washed into them from above, affording excellent grazing and arable land, and the courses of the streams throughout these chalk valleys are marked out by rows of farms, villages, or small towns, in almost continuous succession, with a remarkable prevalence of the place-name suffix -ton along them. Over the higher levels we shall find numerous artificial ponds—bedded with clay and lime

Butser Hill, near Petersfield

(Showing the characteristic broad swell of the chalk)

carefully puddled in—and known as "dew" or "mist" ponds. These are for the cattle and sheep which graze the upland pasture. In the absence of natural springs,

Distribution of Anglo-Saxon Place-names ending in -ton
(*The unshaded areas are chalk, the shaded other formations*)

domestic water supply is obtained from wells, and these are nowadays often provided with small wind-pumps which pump the water up into storage tanks. These pumps, recently introduced, are now quite a marked feature of the landscape all over the chalk upland.

The areas which fringe the chalk plateau north and south are practically identical in geological structure, consisting of a series of clays and sands, but they differ in climate and in rainfall. The elevations throughout both areas are much lower than the central plateau.

Litchfield Down, near Whitchurch, with "mist pond"

The name "Woodlands," given to the northern of these areas, is not derived from the timber which grows upon it, though much of it is under timber or covert, but from the somewhat cold nature of the soil, which favours the growth of wood and covert rather than of crops. The soil varies greatly; where clays predominate the soil is strong, and both timber and general crops flourish, but over much of it there is merely thin sand overlying layers of clay or sometimes what is called "iron-pan," through which water cannot drain, so that dry and stony patches alternate with marsh and water-logged land. Thus here, in contrast with the central core of chalk, it is the upper levels which are the more productive. The streams moreover do not collect so definitely into well-marked valleys, and the villages are not aligned along the river courses but are dotted about confusedly and often at a distance from them.

The Coastal Fringe differs in soil but little from the Woodlands, but it has a southern aspect and a warmer climate. It has a smaller rainfall, is better drained, and is more fertile. The warmer soil and good climatic conditions favour small-fruit cultivation, and strawberry culture is extensively carried on over much of it. The fruit can be marketed very early, and secures good prices, the industry being thus a very profitable one.

The general contours both of the Woodlands and of the coastal fringe, though never bold, present considerable variations. Where clays prevail the contour is flat, but in the sandy areas the surface is very broken. There is nothing of the long even roll of the chalk downs, recalling the broad swell of the open sea.

The New Forest is a district again quite by itself; a region of sands and gravels so poor in character that over the greater part of it cultivation is quite impossible. The general level is low, but very rarely flat, its surface forming broad, slightly heaving curves, with ridges and hollows alternating, and following one another mile after mile. Much of it is open, covered with heather or bracken, with here and there stretches of turf, according to the character of the soil. Much of it is under timber, usually in plantations. Wild life abounds, and portions of the district are a naturalist's paradise.

The Selborne area also has a character quite of its own. Looking out eastward from the top of Noar Hill or Stonor Hill the eye travels for miles and miles over a broad well-wooded plain, flanked southwards by the South Downs. This plain is the extreme western corner of the Weald. The surface, though generally speaking low, undulates greatly. In places it is very broken, and everywhere it is extremely picturesque. Much of it is sandy, and the soil is in parts so thin that it will not support timber—in fact nothing but bracken, gorse, or heather. Part of it is heavy clay land covered with thick wood, especially oak. Hops grow well over a good portion of it, so that it may also be termed the hop region of Hampshire.

5. Water Supply. Drainage. Rivers

On the water supply of any region depend not merely the nature and extent of natural vegetation and of cultivation, but also the distribution of population, the nature of the industrial occupations, and in many cases the communication routes. It is therefore one of the most important factors in determining local characteristics.

Water falls plentifully in the form of rain over the whole of Hampshire, and makes its way continuously to the lower levels by the "visible drainage" of brooks and rivers, or by "invisible drainage" or percolation through the soil below the surface.

When porous or "permeable" strata overlie "impermeable" rock such as stiff clays and the like, the rainfall soaks through the former till its passage is arrested by the impermeable strata, which thus form what is termed a "water-seal." Much of the rainfall which falls on our Hampshire heights collects in natural basins underground and issues as springs at points a considerable distance below and away from the place of catchment.

From various causes, notably the large demands for town water-supply, the "water-table," or saturation level of the underground water is continuously sinking, as is the case over a great part of England. There is evidence indeed that in Roman and Saxon times the springs in the Andover district issued some fifty to sixty feet above their present points of origin.

The great water-bearing formation of Hampshire is the chalk. While the upper chalk is porous and much fissured, the lower chalk strata are stiff and practically impervious, acting as a "water seal" for the layers above. Thus springs are extremely abundant, particularly where these two meet. The soaking through the chalk takes some time, however, and chalk springs usually flow most abundantly some weeks after rain, the immediate effect of rain on them being often negligible. The water of these springs is "hard" (*i.e.* it contains dissolved lime in the form of calcium carbonate) and is very clear and limpid, and as they issue from deep-seated sources the Hampshire chalk springs have a remarkably even temperature—usually about 50° Fahr. throughout both winter and summer. The Hampshire chalk streams flow in well-defined valleys and are fed by numerous affluents, and if we trace these upward we shall find they generally originate in channels or ravines, which are either entirely dry, or along which streams flow intermittently according to season. Such intermittent streams are called "bournes." The Hurstbourne, Headbourne, Somborne, Oxenbourne, Enborne, as well as many streams known merely as Bourne, are examples of this, and their origin will be at once evident from what has been said above. The points at which these bournes first become apparent vary greatly according to season.

Next, but far less important in our county as water-bearing strata, are the sands and gravels. The water is softer and less clear, and is often impregnated with iron, which combines with the presence of peat in the associated strata to turn the water dark and inky—hence the term Blackwater so often applied to streams in the sandy areas. The rivers of this type do not flow in well-defined valleys, like the chalk streams.

Hampshire forms one main drainage area, the "Hampshire basin" proper, but a smaller area to the north drains into the Thames valley, and a diminutive portion near Petersfield into the Sussex basin along the Rother valley. The main watershed of the Hampshire basin follows a zigzag course, which is, roughly, as follows :—

Pilot Hill, Sidown Hill, Beacon Hill, Wootton St Laurence, Church Oakley, Farleigh Wallop, Herriard, Medstead, Lyeway, West Tisted, Privett, Froxfield. At Froxfield, where the three basins meet, it branches, cutting off the Thames basin along a line through Stonor Hill, Warren Corner, Noar Hill, and by a line

The River Test at Mottisfont
(*Showing chalk escarpment east of the valley*)

south of Wolmer Pond to Weaver's Down. The Hampshire and Sussex basins meet along the line from Froxfield, across to the ridge of the South Downs over Butser Hill. The lowest point of the watershed is at Church Oakley, 300 feet above sea level.

The most characteristic Hampshire rivers are the Test and the Itchen, which are Hampshire rivers throughout the whole of their course. Both are typical chalk streams. The Avon is really a Wiltshire stream whose lower course traverses our county to get to the sea. All three flow through well-defined valleys with charming scenery, and are fed by numerous affluents.

These valleys have been slowly but continuously carved out by their rivers, assisted by wind and frost and rain. This erosion of rock or soil is always irregular, so that rivers tend slowly to change their course and to swing backwards and forwards from side to side of their valleys, so that the latter continually widen and deepen as time goes on. On some formations, too, notably chalk, rain-water exerts a directly solvent action which co-operates in producing hollows and depressions. Ages ago the Hampshire land levels were much higher than now—possibly several thousand feet in places. The water supply was more copious. Ice and snow accumulated in winter, the melting of which caused violent floods, and so erosion was far more active then than now. Thus the land became crossed by great valleys and so the Test and Itchen grew, their main streams flowing roughly from north to south. The Test, being the more active, produced more rapid erosion, ultimately cutting below the levels of some of the valleys which drained into the Itchen, thus "capturing" this drainage and causing rivers to flow along entirely new courses. In this way much of the drainage of the northern heights which once fed the Itchen was diverted westward into the Test valley, while the Avon, which probably once flowed direct from Salisbury to Southampton Water, broke out a new channel southward and so attained its present course. The river Rother is again another local example of this process of river capture, the Sussex river Arun having captured it as well as a number of streams which once flowed directly south to the Sussex coast.

The Test has a total length of some 38 miles. Its permanent source is in the water meadows between Overton and Ash at a level of 300 feet above the sea; thus it has an average fall of 9 feet to the mile—a swift stream as compared with the Thames, for example, which has an average fall of about 2½ feet to the mile. Its ultimate source is at Church Oakley, and in wet seasons a continuous stream flows down the valley from this point, but in dry seasons it disappears in "swallow holes" near Deane and wells out again in great springs at Polhampton, Southington, and Laverstoke. At Whitchurch the river broadens out into several branches which pass through marshy meadows, meeting the Bourne at Hurstbourne, and from here by Longparish, Middleton, and Wherwell, right on to Mottisfont, great springs well up. Near Wherwell the Bullington (or Micheldever) flows in on the left and the Anton on the right. The Bullington valley is particularly interesting. The stream rises at Northbrook, and flows along a marshy peat valley through Bullington and Bransbury Common, and the whole district of Longparish, Bransbury, and Wherwell is a veritable land of water, a natural paradise where fish, marsh-haunting birds, and bog plants of every kind abound. The Anton gives its name to Andover, and with its little tributary the Ann or Pillbrook serves to drain a large open area, the head-waters of which are at Appleshaw and Kimpton.

Retracing our steps to the northern edge of the Test area we find an altogether different country, the dry steep slopes of the Northern Downs. Here bare chalk downs with deep combes and valleys and a dry stony soil alternate with patches of woodland and cultivated farms. Of the lateral valleys which debouch into the central valley of the Bourne, the most striking is Netherton valley, which leads from the great hollow of Combe down to Hurstbourne Tarrant—a dry valley filled with a rich alluvial wash along which water once flowed freely, leaving in places great accumulations of flint and rough débris to testify to the activity of former erosion. The permanent headwaters of the Bourne are at Stoke, but in wet seasons a steady stream comes down right from Vernham's Dean. St Mary Bourne lies below Stoke, and here watercress beds abound. The flow of water varies greatly. In March great springs well out, but by August the supply ceases and the stream shrinks to quite small dimensions.

Below Wherwell the Test valley broadens rapidly, the river dividing into numerous channels, and receiving continual reinforcements of springs and tributaries—the Wallop Brook, Somborne, Dean, Tadbourne and others. At Mottisfont, where a Benedictine Abbey once stood, is a beautiful natural spring with a permanent flow yielding some 2,000,000 gallons of water daily. Below Romsey the Test ceases to be a chalk stream and the valley opens out into a broad flood plain, receiving numerous small streams, till the river finally empties itself by two channels into the tidal estuary at Redbridge.

In many ways the Itchen bears a close resemblance to the Test, but economically it is more important from

Stone Bridge over the Test at Redbridge

the great docks lying at its mouth. It has a threefold source, the Itchen proper, the Alre, and the Candover. The Itchen proper rises near Hinton Ampner, 240 feet above sea level, and has a total course of 20 miles—a fall of 12 feet to the mile, which gives it a rapid current. At first shallow, with a succession of springs and swallow-holes, it passes through Cheriton and Tichborne, meets the Alre, and is joined by the Candover just below Alresford. From here to Winchester it divides into several channels, flowing along a broad valley where picturesque villages and hamlets follow in close succession from Itchen Stoke to Headbourne Worthy. This is a regular water-country, with fords or " watersplashes " at numerous points, and mills at short intervals along the stream. At Twyford, below Winchester, the valley widens rapidly, past Otterbourne and Eastleigh, with its big railway construction works. The tidal estuary is flanked by the great Southampton docks on the west, and the shipbuilding yards of Woolston on the east, till finally it loses itself in Southampton Water.

The Avon enters the county just south of Downton in Wilts—where it is liable to considerable flooding at times—and flows through a picturesque valley past Fordingbridge, Ringwood, and Sopley to Christchurch. All round this town are broad water meadows where cattle graze, and here the river joins the Stour to empty into Christchurch Harbour, a wonderful inland lake of great beauty and interest. The actual harbour mouth is at Mudeford, where there is a remarkable bar or bank of shingle which has undergone great changes in form and extent in the last few years. The long narrow entrance is termed the Run, and here salmon are netted in some numbers during the season.

Of other Hampshire streams the Meon is the most marked in character. It rises by springs at Oxenbourne and Southmill, at a level of 400 feet above the sea—the highest chalk springs in Hampshire. As it is only about fifteen miles long, its current is rapid, though the volume is small. At West Meon it is intermittent, as swallow-holes occur, into which the river disappears. There are mills along its course at Droxford and elsewhere. Its estuary is now silted up, and the river enters the sea as an insignificant dribble below Titchfield. The Meon valley is remarkably picturesque, with numerous old villages. In very early Anglo-Saxon days it became peopled by the Meon-wara, a Jutish folk who settled here, probably before the Gewissas occupied the rest of Hampshire.

Eastward of the Meon there are no regular streams but the chalk formation here is highly water-bearing, and characteristic springs or streams more or less intermittent flow out all along the junction of the chalk with the clays and sands above it. These are called *lavants*. They usually issue at various levels after winter rains. In 1879 for instance, and also in 1914–15, great lavants occurred at Hambledon at the head of the Wallington valley. The absence of streams is due to the absorbent character of the chalk, for the water yield of this corner of the county is exceedingly copious. At Bedhampton remarkable springs exist, which yield millions of gallons of water daily, and supply Portsmouth with water. An interesting feature of these is that they are fed from rain which has fallen on the southern slope of the South Downs, and has drained under the clay strata lying south of the chalk, which, being impermeable, have acted as a seal, till the water has finally broken out at a lower level on the southern chalk outcrop close to the shore.

The New Forest streams are of quite different character—they are mainly somewhat ill-defined trickles through marshy and water-logged hollows emptying into winding tidal estuaries. We have already referred to their dark and inky appearance, and to the occurrence of the name Blackwater both here and elsewhere in the county, where similar soil conditions prevail.

The Hampshire streams belonging to the Thames basin are not important. The chief is the Loddon, which rises near Basingstoke not very far from the source of the Test, at the lowest point (300 feet) of the Hampshire watershed. Thus the " divide " between the Test and Loddon valleys is all but imperceptible, and the two valleys indeed form a long uninterrupted trough-like depression, well-watered and fertile, a natural line of crossing of the channels of communication east and west with those going north and south, where the important town Basingstoke has sprung up.

A unique feature of Hampshire is that some part of its water supply is derived from wells sunk under the sea. The forts at Spithead are supplied by deep wells of this character, and the water so obtained is not only used to supply them, but is actually shipped to various points along the coast.

6. Geology

At the time Hampshire began to take shape the east and south of England formed the bed of a shallow sea whose shore stretched north-east from Dorset across the Midlands. Present-day Hampshire and Sussex formed the estuary of a great river which flowed eastward. On the bed of this estuary, during what is known as the Cretaceous Period, the sandy and clayey detritus washed off the land began to accumulate, forming what is now the Lower Greensand, Gault Clay, and Upper Greensand, portions of which we find to-day exposed in the Selborne and Petersfield areas, and also near Sydmonton. Then the ocean grew deeper, the coast receded westward, and a deep sea was formed beneath which much of France and Northern Europe, as well as the greater part of Britain, was submerged. On the floor of this ocean the remains of marine creatures consisting largely of shells of Foraminifera slowly accumulated, forming three types of chalk—the Lower Chalk, impure and mingled with clay and sand; the Middle Chalk, purer and whiter, with occasional flints; and the Upper Chalk, also pure and white, with great deposits of flint, often disposed in layers. Later, this sea-bed slowly rose, and earthy matter, the result of land erosion, again collected on it, and thus the Eocene rocks of the Tertiary period were deposited—a series of clays and sands known as the Woolwich and Reading Beds, the London Clay, and the Bagshot Beds, covering Hampshire, Sussex, Kent, and part of the Thames valley. A period of shrinkage followed—the Cretaceous and Eocene rocks were crushed in together from the south, causing the sea bottom to bulge and curve, and forming a series of ridges and hollows with their long axes roughly east and west. Thus the central ridges of Hampshire and the Isle of Wight

Post Tertiary.	Recent (Neolithic) or later.	Peat. alluvium, shingle, loose sand.
		Brick Earth.
Tertiary.	Pleistocene (Palæolithic) and Pliocene.	Valley Gravels.
		Newer Plateau Gravels.
		Clay-with-flints.
		Older Plateau Gravels.
	Oligocene or Fluvio-Marine.	Headon Beds—sands and clays.
		Barton Beds (white sand).
	Eocene.	Barton clays (blue with numerous fossils).
		Bracklesham Beds (sands and clays).
		Bagshot Beds (sands and clays).
		London Clay (blue clay).
		Reading Beds (red mottled clays with sands and pebble beds).
Secondary.	Upper Cretaceous.	Upper Chalk—(soft and white with numerous flints).
		Middle Chalk (harder, white with occasional flints).
		Lower Chalk (gray and marly—impervious).
		Upper Greensand (ferruginous sand with chert nodules).
		Gault (stiff blue clay with marl and sand).
	Lower Cretaceous.	Folkestone Beds (ferruginous sand).
		Sandgate Beds (sand and clay).
		Hythe Beds (greenish ferruginous sand with chert nodules and limestone bands (Bargate stone).

slowly emerged and became dry land, while a series of beds known as the Oligocene or Fluvio-Marine were deposited in the trough between. As successive layers emerged erosion and denudation again became active, but the upheaval continued and Hampshire came into being. Whether the later Tertiary strata ever formed a continuous sheet or cap over the whole chalk area we do not know, as during emergence marine erosion must have competed with upheaval, but at all events active denudation began to remove the upper layers, if not to lay bare the chalk itself. Rivers began to carve out the valleys along lines somewhat as we see them to-day, and Hampshire began to assume its present shape, a core of chalk thrown into folds, with Tertiary sands and clays in the troughs between. The coast line was of chalk, extending eastward from Studland on a line considerably south of the present Isle of Wight coast; and the Solent and Southampton Water of to-day formed parts of a big river system flowing in an easterly direction with its mouth somewhere near Brighton.

Since then, though changes of level have occurred, there has been no general submergence of the whole area. The general change has been to wear away the upper layers, sometimes so completely that not only has the Tertiary cap in many places been entirely got rid of, but much of the chalk has been removed also, while in others small Tertiary patches or outliers still remain *in situ*. The river valleys have grown deeper and wider, and the general land level has been lowered enormously,

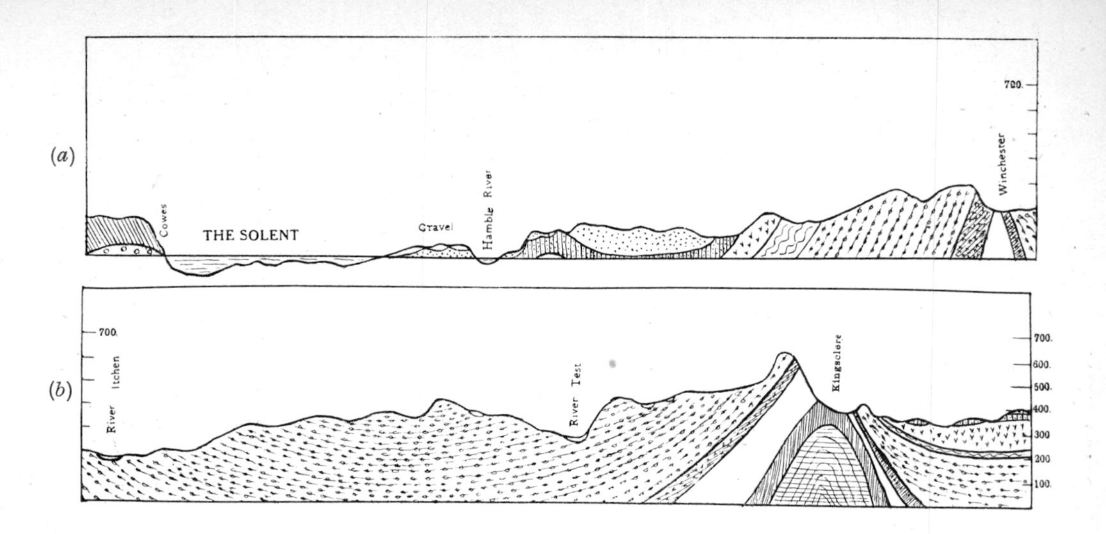

Geological Section N. and S. across County, passing close to Cowes, Winchester, and Kingsclere: (*b*) is a continuation of (*a*)

(*The figures indicate height above sea level in feet*)

possibly several thousand feet. What is left as the result of these erosive processes are mainly clayey or gravelly deposits; such as the "hazel loam" and "clay-with-flints," which at numerous points overlie the chalk sub-soil; the extensive sheets of pebbly gravel, known as plateau gravel; the river gravels deposited in terraces along the valleys; and the alluvial deposits of the river beds.

No less remarkable are the climatic changes which have occurred during these alternations of land surface. Two periods of intense cold known as the First and Second Glacial Epochs followed the emergence of Hampshire, but our county was never covered with ice, for the ice cap did not descend south of the Thames. All vegetation, however, except plants of Arctic type, perished, and the flora of to-day is the result of slow creeping back of different species during the later temperate periods. It was probably during this epoch that man first appeared on the scene, and his earliest remains occur in the form of rudely fashioned stone implements found to-day for the most part in the river gravels.

Changes of coastal form have also been profound. The great river estuary already mentioned was fed by two main systems—the Avon, with the Test and Itchen as its affluents, emptied itself along the Southampton Water, while the Solent, fed by the Frome, Stour, and Isle of Wight rivers joined it near the Cowes of to-day. Between the upper Solent and the sea was a barrier of chalk, elevated but not wide, stretching from Studland to south of St Catherine's Point. The scour of the tide along the Dorset coast steadily cut this chalk back more and more, while the continued pitting and swinging of the Solent across its valley deepened the river bed, till finally the chalk barrier gave way, and the Solent became an arm of the sea. The chalk sea-wall once broken through, erosion of the soft Bournemouth sands proceeded swiftly—the sea coast was cut back northwards, the Lower Avon deepened its bed and its gradient grew continuously steeper, till finally it "captured" the water-flow from the higher levels, and the whole Avon system was diverted into its present course.

So far we have dealt mainly with the foundation strata or "Solid Geology" as it is termed, but above these lie extensive sheets of surface deposits known as "Drift," the result of erosion and redistribution of the uppermost layers of soil. The erosive effect of water on chalk is not merely mechanical—the washing away of matter—but a direct solvent or chemical action takes place as well, and this, exerted both on and below the surface, is one of the chief causes of the deep hollows and rounded depressions found everywhere on the Chalk Downs, the best Hampshire example being the "Punchbowl" at Chesford Head, near Winchester. But while this solvent action has removed much of the chalk of the upper layers, it has left behind enormous masses of flint and other insoluble matter. In this way the soil usually found covering the chalk has been formed. We have spoken of the "hazel loam" and

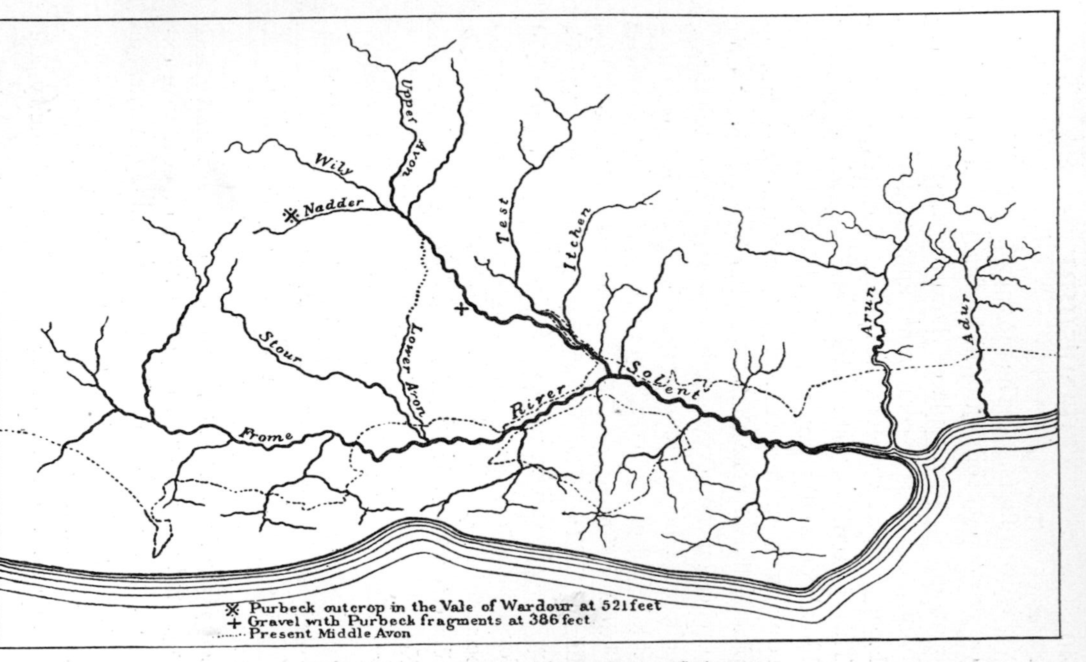

The Basin of the ancient River Solent

(*Present coast-line in pecked line*)

"clay-with-flints." The former is a light, stony, easily-worked soil in which small weathered flints abound. In many places, however, a stiff dark red-brown clayey soil containing angular flint-stones in large quantities occurs, instead of the "hazel loam." This is termed "clay-with-flints" and is probably broken down Tertiary matter mingled with undissolved scourings from the chalk. It is found in isolated patches practically all over the chalk plateau, sometimes even perched on the very summits, as for instance at Linkenholt, at a height of over 700 feet, and above Combe at a height of 900 feet. On the eastern side of the chalk plateau it forms an extensive sheet from Froxfield and Filmer Hill to beyond Medstead, as is well shown by the widespread use of flint in this area as material for building. The "Plateau gravel" also mentioned occurs in patches over the upper levels, *e.g.* at Silchester, but its main development is over the New Forest, where it forms great sheets. "Valley gravels" occur mainly in terraces fringing the river valleys, as near Romsey on the Test, and the marshy valley bottoms contain considerable quantities of peat. All these gravels are deeply impregnated with iron, which gives them their rich ruddy colour. Solvent action by air and water, however, tends to remove this iron, and the upper layers of gravels, especially in exposed places, frequently become entirely bleached. In the New Forest the exposed gravel is sometimes almost dead white.

The characteristics of the Drift in this county are

extremely variable, and local industries, such as pottery and brick-making, as well as agriculture, depend as much, or even more on it than on the solid geology. Sudden changes of conditions are frequent, and on one and the same farm the soil may vary from light sand and loam to heavy clay, while close at hand may be chalk down covered with dry pasture.

The characteristics of the chalk plateau have been sufficiently indicated—the broad swelling curves, the dry hollows and combes, and the deeper valleys watered by clear streams. The Tertiary formations to the south and north call for no detailed discussion here, but the Selborne (Middle and Lower Cretaceous) area presents characters quite distinct from the rest of the county. Selborne itself is on the Lower Chalk, but east of it the older beds crop out in well-defined belts, Upper Greensand, Gault, and Lower Greensand. The first named is highly ferruginous, and blocks of ironstone, often of considerable size, are of frequent occurrence. Along with it are found strata of "malmstone"—a hard sandy rock, locally also termed firestone or freestone. The Gault, which succeeds the Upper Greensand, forms a narrow belt curving from Bentley to Petersfield—a stiff, dark blue clay impervious to water. The Lower Greensand series—Folkstone, Sandgate, and Hythe Beds are also ferruginous, the last-named containing a hard stone called chert, and beds of hard sandy limestone known as Bargate stone, formerly in great request for building. The surface characters of this district are very marked and interesting. The chalk plateau ends in a sharp high ridge, from which beds of malmstone protrude in terraces, the whole forming a steep escarpment or land cliff running north and south. Land slides are frequent, as the Gault clay beneath retains the moisture and forms a slippery surface on which the upper layer creeps continuously downwards. Thus the surface of the fields is curiously billowy, landmarks are subject to slow continual movement, and hedgerows once straight become wavy and curving. The big landslide near Hawkley in 1774 is mentioned by Gilbert White.

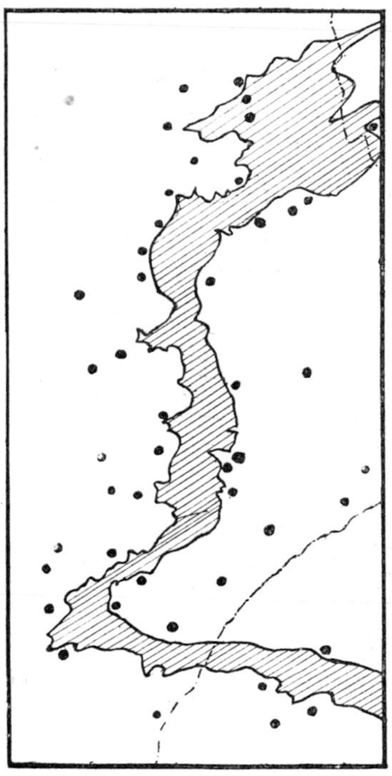

Diagram showing fewness of Settlements in the Gault area in E. Hants

(*Shaded area = Gault*)

The various formations are clearly marked not only by the general character of their contours, but also by their vegetation and other surface features. The weathered malmstone of the Upper Greensand, enriched by washings of marl from the Lower Chalk above, forms an excellent medium for hop culture, and a line of villages, Binsted, East Worldham, Selborne, Empshott and Hawkley follow along the Greensand outcrop. But, once the Gault to the east is reached, the surface changes to rich open grassland covered with dense patches of woodland, almost exclusively oak, which here revels in the strong heavy soil. The Gault belt was probably one of the last areas in the county to become inhabited, as the heavy impervious soil defied the rude cultivation of early days, and villages are even now almost entirely absent along its length. But immediately the Gault is passed a line of settlements again appears, Kingsley, Oakhanger, Blackmoor, Greatham, Liss, and Petersfield marking the water-line along the Lower Greensand outcrop. The Folkestone Beds form a " hungry, sandy, barren waste " as Gilbert White phrases it ; the Sandgate Beds are less permeable, and marshy spots abound in them ; while open heath and mingled timber mark the Hythe Beds. Few parts can compare with this in picturesqueness, and the rich growth of bracken, furze, and heather of Weaver's Down and Liphook are a glorious sight in autumn.

Of the Tertiary outliers, of which we have spoken, the best marked is Horsedown Common, near Crondall. Another interesting local feature is the occurrence of large masses of hardened sandstone or conglomerate known locally as Sarsen stones or Grey-wethers. A large one occurs near Twyford, and many are—or were—to be found in the Froxfield area. Years ago they were much more numerous, but they have now been largely broken up for road metal and building material. An interesting evidence of change of level is the raised sea-beach, now 140 feet above the sea, best shown near the Nelson Monument on Portsdown, and traceable at points along the Test and Itchen valleys, as well as eastward along the coast as far as Goodwood in Sussex.

7. Natural History

We have already seen how, during the Ice Age, glacial conditions prevailed over Britain, thus destroying all plants save those of Arctic type. When temperate conditions returned a slow re-establishment of vegetation took place from the European mainland, to which Britain was at that time joined, and the present flora, like the fauna, of our land is thus of similar general character to that of the continent of Europe.

Hampshire presents a great diversity of soil and climate, so that we should naturally expect a considerable richness of species whether of plants or animals. But, in addition to this, the untouched nature of much of the county, its extensive open heaths and woodlands, its marshes and bogs both in the New Forest and elsewhere, have made much of it practically a "reserve" or "sanctuary," wherein survive many forms of animal, bird, or plant life which

Sarsen Stone at Shawford, near Winchester

human interference has elsewhere rendered rare or extinct.

There are nearly 1200 species of flowering plants found in Hampshire, and of these a good number have their chief range within the county limits. Thus about 180 species found in Hampshire are absent from both Wiltshire and Berkshire, 150 from the Isle of Wight, 120 from Surrey, and about 60 from both Dorset and Sussex. Most noticeable perhaps, of all, are the great timber trees which spread over so much of the county, and the hedge timber, some of it not improbably the remains of the primeval forest which once covered nearly the whole area. Along the chalk upland, the beech is the most conspicuous tree—though here and there the yew vies with it—and many of the highest points are crowned with a clump or possibly a dense wood of beeches. These beech woods, too, in many places, clothe the sides of the chalk slopes, forming the well-known "hangers" or hanging woods, of which Selborne Hanger is perhaps the best known. The finest beech wood is Mark Ash in the New Forest, and the beeches in Hackwood Park are also remarkable for their size.

Equally characteristic in its way is the yew—sometimes called the "Hampshire weed,"—found mainly, but not exclusively, on chalky soil. It is widely diffused over the central, northern, and north-eastern parts of the county, and is conspicuous on the grand chalk downs from Butser to Old Winchester Hill. In ancient times it was extensively planted, and nearly every

Yew Trees on the Chalk, near Crab Wood, Winchester

Hampshire churchyard has its yew tree, while wonderful hedges and topiary work of this tree are common in Hampshire gardens. Among the larger and more famous churchyard yews are the yew at Selborne, which in 1879 measured 24½ feet in circumference 4 feet from the ground, that at South Hayling, and the

Cottages near Hursley

(*Yew and Beech on the chalk slopes above*)

enormous clipped yew at Twyford. An avenue of ancient giant yews lines one of the roads at Preston Candover. A quite characteristic Hampshire view will show the chalk slopes bearing beech and yew above, and at the bottom of the hollow a hamlet or cluster of buildings, with elm, sycamore, or chestnut revealing the presence of a deeper soil. The oak is common, especially in the New Forest, and the areas of the London Clay and Gault are marked by the splendid oak belts which cover them. Alice Holt Forest is almost entirely composed of this tree. The largest oak in the New Forest is the Knightwood Oak, three miles from Lyndhurst.

Knightwood Oak
(Largest Oak in the New Forest)

Few trees in the county are more widespread than the Scotch fir, which forms extensive belts all along the sandy soils and spreads naturally with remarkable quickness. Whether it is native to the county or not is a debated question, but much has been planted, and the whole district of Bournemouth has within a hundred years or so become covered with magnificent fir woods. All over the New Forest great plantations of it exist, and the trees planted closely together send up long straight stems specially useful for telegraph poles.

The most characteristic hedgerows are those which outline the cultivation limit along the lower edges of much of the Chalk Downs, particularly along the northern heights of the county. Many of these, as has been already pointed out, are of natural growth. Equally characteristic, too, on these slopes is the juniper, found widespread on the open down all over the chalk country.

The sea-shore plants alone form a numerous series: the sandy cliffs or dunes of Bournemouth and Hayling; the mud flats of Lymington and Beaulieu estuaries, of Portsmouth and Langston Harbours and Southampton Water; the dry shingle of Calshot Spit; all have their characteristic flora. One leading and most useful sand plant is the Marram grass (*Ammophila arundinacea*), spreading by creeping root-stocks, some three feet deep, and holding the thin sand together. It is found in sandy places along the shore, from Boscombe as far as Hayling Island. The mud flats along the river estuaries at Beaulieu, Hythe, Southampton Water, etc., are covered with great growths of cord grass (*Spartina stricta*). An interesting species of this, the many-spiked cord grass (*Spartina alterniflora*), with the sub-species *Spartina Townsendi* has established itself now for many years at Southampton. Other familiar and characteristic sand and shore species are the prickly sea holly (*Eryngium maritimum*), with its pale blue leaves, the sea pink (*Armeria vulgaris*), sea lavender (*Statice Limonium*), sea-blite (*Suæda maritima*) and the sea—or horned—poppy (*Glaucium luteum*). Along the shore from Exbury to Calshot the sea-kale is still found abundantly. At one time immense quantities grew on Calshot Spit, and here the shore folk used to cover the young shoots with shingle to blanch them for the market. Curtis, the naturalist, author of the *Flora Londiniensis,* first tried the experiment of cultivating the sea-kale, and the new vegetable soon became popular on the London market. Another indigenous vegetable, *Beta maritima,* the sea-beet, grows everywhere along the shingle, and is probably the parent of our garden beet and mangold wurzels. Here and there too along the shore, as at Mudeford and Hayling, the samphire (*Crithmum maritimum*) occurs, though never plentifully. It is much more abundant in the Isle of Wight, and samphire gathering, for pickling or perfume making, was formerly a distinct industry. Among the rare plants are the two species of beard grass (*Polypogon monspeliensis,* and *P. littoralis*), which are found on the salt marshes at Portchester and Portsea. The Hampshire shore plants are in fact extremely interesting.

By many of the Hampshire streams the giant musk (*Mimulus luteus*), an American plant naturalised here, is found brightening the banks in summer with great splashes of brilliant yellow. Another American introduction is the water thyme (*Elodea Canadensis*), which within the last sixty years or so has spread everywhere along the streams. A plant now comparatively rare is the buckbean (*Menyanthes trifoliata*), but the cotton grass (*Eriophorum polystachium*) with its little white tufts nodding over the swamps, is common. All three species of sundew (*Drosera*) are widely diffused, forming ruddy patches on the peaty soil of the swamps, and the butterwort (*Pinguicula vulgaris*) and more than one species of bladderwort (*Utricularia*) are to be met with in the ponds and ditches. Of the specially uncommon species the purple gladiolus (*Gladiolus illyricus*) and the Isnardia (*Ludwigia palustris*) have their chief range in the New Forest in England, and the summer lady's-tresses (*Spiranthes æstivalis*) occurs only in Hampshire and in Wyre Forest, Worcester.

Over the dry chalk pastures, such plants as the rock-rose (*Helianthemum vulgare*), milk-wort, red, white, or blue, (*Polygala vulgaris*), squinancy-wort (*Asperula cynanchica*), drop-wort (*Spiraea Filipendula*) and salad burnet (*Poterium Sanguisorba*) are among the most characteristic. Over the sandy stretches of Wolmer and the New Forest we find the heaths growing freely, as well as the yellow broom and the two species of gorse. In the same districts the whortleberry (*Vaccinium Myrtillus*) abounds: its berries are gathered by the country folk and find a ready sale. The cranberry (*Oxycoccus palustris*) is found in bogs near Liss and Selborne.

Hampshire is peculiarly an orchid county, no less than twenty-nine species occurring. Among the woodland types are the butterfly orchis (*Habenaria bifolia* and *Habenaria chlorantha*), the white helleborine (*Cephalanthera grandiflora*), tway-blade (*Listera ovata*), and others, while over the dry chalk pastures we find the bee orchis (*Ophrys apifera*), the fly orchis (*Ophrys muscifera*), the fragrant orchis (*Gymnadenia Conopsea*), and the frog orchis (*Habenaria viridis*), as well as many other species.

Hampshire still possesses the finest of all our native wild animals—the red deer, although they are now but very few in number, probably not more than a score. Fallow deer, however, are abundant in the New Forest, and seem to be of a somewhat unusual type, the horns showing a tendency to fork into points. In winter the animals are dark brown, but assume in summer the spots and the coloration associated with their name. Roe-deer also exist, but in no great number: they are believed to be descendants of migrants from Dorset some fifty years ago. The badger is widely distributed in the woodlands, and the otter is hunted regularly along many of the Hampshire streams. Of the New Forest ponies, which live in a semi-feral state, we shall have to speak later.

As from its position and conditions might be predicted, the county is rich in bird life. As it is maritime, the sea birds are well represented, and its creeks and great mud flats afford excellent localities for the various ducks, waders, and waterfowl, and are in consequence a favourite resort of the punt-gunner. Its proximity to the Continent, as in the case of Sussex and other of the Channel counties, brings it a number of southern visitors of the rarer kinds, such as the bee-eater, golden oriole, roller, and hoopoe—the latter, indeed, is almost a regular spring arrival, and has even bred. Its physical conditions, too, being of such varied nature, favour a corresponding richness in the number of species. As Mr Trevor Battye points out in his Introduction to the "Natural History," section of the *Victoria County*

History, " it would be hard to imagine a clearer natural contrast than that between the juniper-dotted, wind-swept hills of the Hampshire highland and the rather tepid condition of the New Forest, laden with vegetation and filled with springs, streams, and bogs," and this difference is exemplified in its plants and animals. On the northern uplands we find such birds as the Norfolk plover and the dotterel, though the latter is now a rarity. The New Forest is almost without a rival in our land as a sanctuary, and it abounds in plants, birds, and insects of interest and rarity. Another feature of the county is the occurrence of shallow sheets of water, or " Ponds," of which Fleet Pond is the best example, and these, too, are tenanted by a more or less special fauna and flora. The numerous marshy meadows tend to add still further to the long list of species.

Beginning with the birds of prey we find the buzzard is vanishing, the honey buzzard no longer breeds, and the hobby is becoming scarcer, but the peregrine is still far from uncommon. Blackgame are still to be found in certain localities. Of late there has been considerable increase in the numbers of many of the small birds, notably the starling ; and the hawfinch, too, as in other parts of England, has multiplied. The tufted duck is becoming more common, and breeds regularly in various places. In some seasons the cross-bill is very numerous, attracted by the plantations of conifers, and they often nest, especially in the neighbourhood of Bournemouth. At one time that beautiful bird, the bearded tit, used to frequent the Avon, but it has long since departed. Two other rarities, however, there are—the waxwing and the woodchat shrike—which occur sporadically in winter and summer respectively. There are several heronries in the county, and the great crested grebe breeds in the Fleet and other ponds. Fine collections of Hampshire birds may be seen in the museums of Christchurch and Winchester College. There is no special feature concerning the reptiles of the county which calls for remark except that the natterjack toad (*Bufo calamita*), easily recognisable by the yellow line down its back, is found locally in some abundance. The adder is common, especially in the New Forest.

As a trout-fishing county few are more famous than Hampshire, and the Itchen and Test are especially notable rivers. The trout occurs practically in all the streams suitable for it, but the grayling is confined to the Test, Itchen, and Avon. At one time salmon were abundant in the rivers of the county, but this is no longer the case. For some time past they have been decreasing in numbers, but they are still found in the three rivers just mentioned, as well as in the Stour.

The New Forest, as might be supposed, is a remarkably good collecting-ground, not only for Lepidoptera, but also for beetles, of which there are many rare species, and several that are found nowhere else.

8. The Coast. Tides. Erosion.

Though Hampshire is a maritime county, it may almost be described as a maritime county without a coast line, for along more than half of its length the shore is protected from the direct influence of the sea by the Isle of Wight, so that only between Bournemouth and Hurst Castle on the western side, and at Hayling Island on the eastern does it lie directly open to the Channel. It is this that gives the maritime waters of Hampshire the special character of being practically inland waters.

Furthermore, the rock formation of the whole coast is everywhere of a soft and yielding nature. Hence only at the Bournemouth end are there any cliffs worth speaking of, and only at Hengistbury Head is there a promontory of anything like boldness of form. From the landscape point of view, apart from Hengistbury Head, the Isle of Wight dominates everything. Nevertheless there is much to attract and very much to interest along the Hampshire coast, and several extremely important problems of tide and of coastal change can be studied here as they can in no other place.

The coast of Hampshire consists of a foreshore of sand or shingle, with here and there cliffs of very moderate elevation, intersected at intervals all along its length by river estuaries, either funnel-shaped or broadened out into lagoons. The cliffs along the western extremity from Bournemouth and Hengistbury to Milford-on-Sea are of sand and clay, and are cut by deep, winding ravines called "Chines" at Bournemouth, and "Bunneys" further east. Everywhere else we find either mud banks or a foreshore covered with shingle, though from Fareham to Cosham there is a bold cliff or escarpment fronting the shore some miles inland. Along their shores these estuaries are fringed with great

Branksome Chine, near Bournemouth

mud-banks, mostly covered with the characteristic long coast grass, *Spartina*. Christchurch Harbour forms a kind of lagoon to the west; Portsmouth, Langston, and Chichester Harbour a continuous lagoon with some large islands in it to the east; and between them are the funnel-shaped estuaries of Lymington and Beaulieu, and of the Test, Itchen, and Hamble—the latter three all opening into Southampton Water. Between the Isle of Wight and the mainland come the Solent and Spithead—both of them inland waters, Spithead having the character of a roadstead, and the Solent rather that of a broad river, so much so indeed that sailors always

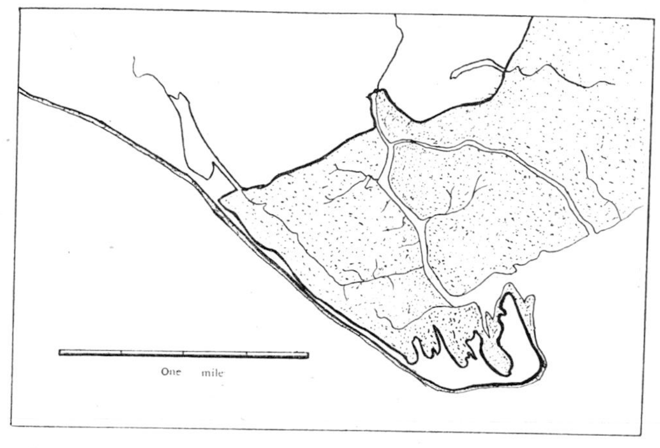

Shingle Spit (1½ miles long) at Western End of Solent

(*Hurst Castle is at the eastern end of the spit, with mud flats in the sheltered area to the east. Illustrates law of eastward drift*)

speak of it as "The River." Place this soft and estuarine coast, these waterways and the Isle of Wight in the middle of a trumpet-shaped sea, the English Channel, broadening out to the west, and we have the problem of tide and coastal loss or gain clearly before us.

To understand this problem we must first study the tidal action of the Channel as a whole. While particular local conditions are very complex, one main principle operates everywhere—the law of Eastward Drift. The tidal wave rising in the Atlantic causes a broad swell over the wide mouth of the Channel from Brest to the Land's End, which passes up Channel as up a narrowing funnel, each point of the coast serving, as the wave reaches it, as the centre of a fresh tidal pulse, in accordance with the well-known laws of wave motion. Eastward the wave sweeps with a scour that grows in intensity the further it advances, carrying with it the loose stones, shingle, and sand that lie round the shore, and cutting into the base of the foreshore as it goes. When the tide falls the conditions are reversed, but the receding waters flow from a narrow channel towards an ever-widening one, and though the scour westward serves to some extent to move the sand and shingle back again, it does so with diminished force. Thus, every tide tending to carry eastward more material than it brings back, the detritus is continually being transported eastward.

The material of the beach at any particular spot will depend on the kind of rocks to the westward of it, but its coarseness or fineness depends on the intensity of scour. The coarser the material the more rapidly it is deposited; the finer it is, the longer it remains in a state of suspension, only settling in comparatively smooth water. At a point or headland directly in the line of scour we shall perhaps find no beach at all; where the scour is less direct we shall find shingle; and only in sheltered areas where the flow is very slack shall we find fine sand or mud. Thus the parts where there is rapid scour are points of erosion, and those of quiescence tend to be points of deposition, and all along the Channel the estuaries and lagoons tend to silt up and sandbanks to form in quieter spots away from shore.

These points are well illustrated in many parts of the Hampshire coast. At the mouths of Christchurch Harbour, at Hurst Castle, Beaulieu River, Calshot, Portsmouth Harbour, and to a less extent at Langston and Chichester Harbours we find long low spits of shingle and sand all running out eastward and more or less of the same character, while round the north-east corner of each there is usually a patch of quiet water where mud flats tend to form. These spits of shingle, whose mode of formation will be readily understood from what has gone before, are not of course confined to Hampshire, as Chesil Beach exhibits the same characteristics in a very marked way. Hurst and Calshot are the best examples of these Hampshire spits, and the advantage they possess for defensive purposes was early recognised.

More remarkable, however, than either of these, from the rapid variations of form and extent it is liable to assume, is the natural mole or shingle bank that lies athwart the mouth of Christchurch Harbour. Formed from the wear of Bournemouth and Hengistbury, it extended in 1910 as a low bank between one and two miles in length, and with a width of from 80 to 200 yards, roughly parallel to the shore, leaving a long narrow

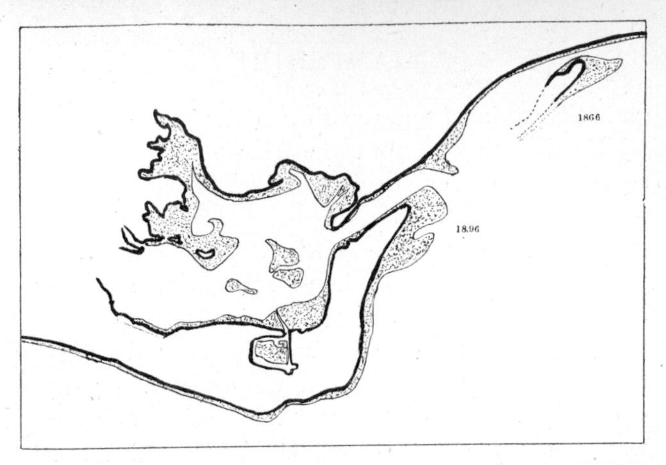

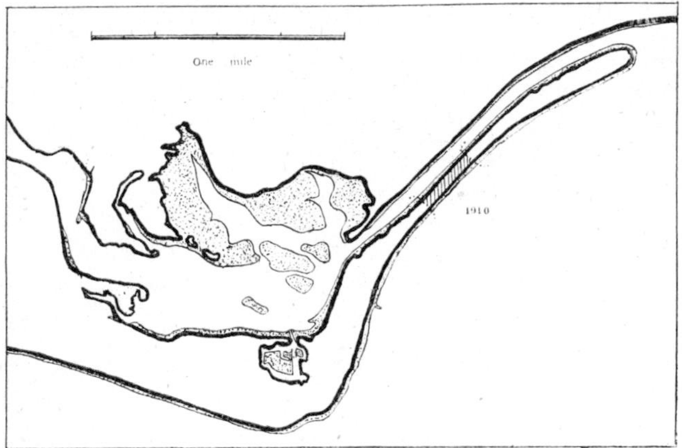

Diagrams illustrating alternate rapid growth and destruction of Sandbank at mouth of Christchurch Harbour since 1866

(*The detached portion in upper figure, marked* 1866, *shows the limit of the sandbank at that date. In* 1896 *it had diminished as indicated by the figure* 1896. *In* 1910 *it had grown again, when a breach was made (indicated by the shading,* 1910), *and the whole eastern end ultimately disappeared. The bank is again developing at the eastern end.*

The dark lines indicate high-water mark, and the light lines low-water mark, ordinary tides.)

channel varying from 100 to 200 yards in width along which the outflow from the Harbour passed to the sea. In December 1910 exceptionally high seas broke through the bank close to Christchurch Harbour, and the breach became the outlet to the sea. In less than twelve months the bank again began to develop, and it is gradually working eastward once more.

In the inland waters of Hampshire we find a different set of tidal conditions from those prevailing n the open Channel. We have what is commonly termed the "double tide." The general tidal movement making from the westward is split at the Needles, and while part of the flood passes up the Solent, the main body sweeps round the south of the island and enters Spithead from the east, reacting with the other body of water and thus causing two periods of maximum high water. The intervals between the two maxima are as follows:—

Solent.	*Spithead.*
Cowes, 60′	Hythe, 77′
Beaulieu, 110′	Southampton, 97′
Lymington, 110′	Redbridge, 110′
Yarmouth, 120′	Calshot, 55′
Hurst, 120′	
Christchurch, 150′	

During the period between the two maxima the variation of depth is very slight—thus at Porstmouth the time required for a variation of one foot at high water is 2 hours, and at Lee 2½ hours, but at Calshot, Hamble, Netley, Hythe, and Southampton it is about 3½ hours,

These figures show us that while in Spithead the effect of this double tide, as it is called, is merely that of prolonged high water, along Southampton Water and the Solent two definite maxima are reached, the intervals between them increasing as we get farther from Spithead. Nor is the effect of this confined to the Solent; it is felt, though with diminishing intensity, as far along the coast as Portland, the interval increasing progressively the farther west we go. At Weymouth the double tide corresponds with low water instead of high water, and Weymouth has therefore a double low tide, known locally as the "Gulder."

The double tide, by prolonging high water in Southampton Water and the adjacent channels, has been a material feature in the commercial development of the port of Southampton. It has been noted as a peculiarity of our coast by the earliest observers, and Bede, writing in the eighth century, gives a description of the phenomenon which is as correct as it is vivid.

While little can as a rule be done permanently to arrest erosion, it can often be delayed and sometimes entirely checked in certain spots by building sea walls and groynes. The latter are barriers of timber or stone running out to seaward from the foreshore at right angles. The sea-borne detritus, *e.g.* shingle and sand, collects on these groynes, heaping itself at first up the western side (law of Eastward Drift) until perhaps the whole is finally covered. When this is the case the groynes remain as a permanent barrier guarding the foreshore from erosion at its base. It will thus be seen that the cartage of shingle from the foreshore is highly inadvisable, as it removes its most efficient protection.

The chief erosion spots along the Hampshire coast are from Southbourne to Hurst on the west and Hayling on the east. At Bournemouth erosion has been going on at the rate of about one foot a year, and at Hengistbury Head and Highcliffe the coast has been cut back during the last sixty or seventy years to the depth of from 12 to 15 feet a year.

There is a considerable quantity of ironstone at Hengistbury, and this was at one time collected from the foreshore as well as quarried, and was shipped to Wales for smelting. This removal of loose material has been very injurious to the whole locality. The huge sandbank at this spot has not only rendered Christchurch Harbour useless for commerce, but by directing the outflow of the river against the cliffs at Highcliffe it is threatening to undermine them. Moreover, the bar at the mouth keeps up the level and so tends to cause submergence of the low-lying grazing lands higher up the river.

Further east from Hordle and Milford a rapid wasting of the coast is again experienced, the shingle being carried towards Hurst, while the finer detritus settles out in the channel forming the great sandbank called Shingles Ledge, a part of which, called Dolphin Bank, is exposed at low tides. The position of this bank, owing to tidal changes, is very variable, and it is sometimes spoken of as the "Moving Island." Within the Solent the mud flats off Lymington and Beaulieu are in a sheltered area, but even so the soft mud is liable to be washed away at times of specially high tide. Off Beaulieu these mud flats are growing in extent, as deposition is assisted by the recent growth on them of the *Spartina*, known locally as rice-grass. From Beaulieu River to Calshot the scour is more active, and here groynes have been erected to arrest the movement of the shingle.

At Hayling Island again erosion is active—at one place in East Stoke Bay the sea is said to have encroached 63 feet between 1904 and 1907. Indeed, large areas of Hayling Island have been lost in historic times, and the land where the earlier church stood has been submerged. Groynes have been erected by private owners in Hayling Bay, and appear to have a satisfactory effect.

While erosion is thus active at certain parts of our coast, it has been counterbalanced at others by reclamation of the foreshore. This, in the quieter areas where natural deposition tends to occur, can be carried out by erecting barriers to seaward and draining the land so recovered. Thus, at Southampton, the dock and railway companies have in recent years reclaimed 180 acres and the Corporation 22, while at Lymington the railway company have reclaimed 100 acres. The greatest local reclamation in recent years has been in the Isle of Wight—viz. that of Brading Harbour. Including the Isle of Wight, Hampshire lost 198 acres by erosion between 1856 and 1897, but gained 852 acres by reclamation—a difference of one square mile.

The navigation of our Hampshire channels and waterways is greatly affected by the sandbanks and their tendency to shift, and were it not for the special tidal conditions already discussed Southampton Water would very possibly be comparatively unnavigable. As it is, its deep water channel or fairway (5 fathoms) contracts in places to very narrow dimensions. Off Calshot itself it is barely a quarter of a mile wide, and from that point it takes a course south-west, so that ocean-going steamers leaving Southampton Water bear right over towards Cowes whether proceeding down Spithead or the Solent. All through Spithead sandbanks occur, marked by bell buoys or lightships, and off Portsmouth there are others, on some of which forts have been erected—Horse Sand, No Man's Land, Spit Fort, etc.

Lighthouses and lightships are numerous. The Needles, Hurst, Egypt Point at Cowes, Calshot, the Warner, and the Nab are among the best known. Of these the Needles Lighthouse and Hurst are the most important. Both of them are occulting, and visible about 15 miles.

The possibility of the existence in Roman times of a ford or even an actual land connection between Gurnard Bay in the Isle of Wight and the mainland at Stone Point is a question which has been much discussed. Numerous traditions and some direct evidence favour it, and a Roman road ran from Dibden, near Hythe, to Stone Point. Although the greatest depth of the intervening channel is as much as 66 feet, the soundings are known to have increased by 10 feet in the last 150 years.

9. Climate

While by "weather" we mean the particular atmospheric conditions of the moment, the word "climate" sums up their general tendency and results, together with the seasonal changes usually experienced over a series of years. Temperature, wind, rain and snow, dew, cloud, humidity, and sunshine are among the chief factors in connection with climate.

The chief conditions on which climatic phenomena depend are :—

(i.) Latitude.

(ii.) The general character of the air-currents.

(iii.) Position in relation to land and sea masses, including elevation.

We may consider these three for a moment. Latitude is, naturally, a very potent factor. Roughly speaking, of course, the nearer a place is to the Equator the warmer it is, and the nearer the Pole, the colder. But there are many exceptions to this rule, and we find the points of greatest heat and cold to coincide with neither of these, but to occur in the middle of large continents like Africa and Australia and in north-east Siberia respectively. In some places the isotherms may even run north and south instead of east and west.

Wind or air-flow is always from areas of high barometric pressure to those of lower pressure, and the British Isles lie between two large areas of fairly constant pressure—a high pressure area over Central Europe, and a low pressure area between Iceland and Greenland. The difference of pressure between these two areas causes a general circulation of air of a rotary character, which drifts over these islands mainly from south-west to north-east. But as Great Britain is at the border of Europe (a great land mass) and the Atlantic Ocean (a great sea mass) over each of which quite different systems of climate prevail, it is very largely a matter of chance, as it were, what type of conditions we shall be affected by at any particular moment—the oceanic or the continental. When the former prevail, low pressure rotary systems, known as cyclones, pass over the country. Pressure being lowest in the centre, the wind sweeps inwards, and precipitation, producing rain or snow, follows. When the continental type prevails we have high pressure systems, or anticyclones, in which, pressure being highest at the centre, the wind blows centrifugally and precipitation is practically impossible. Cyclonic conditions are marked by variable winds, changing weather, and rain; anticyclonic by clear skies, little wind, and no rain. It is the peculiar position of Great Britain, on the debateable area or no-man's land between two regions over which these two systems operate, that causes the extreme variableness and proverbial fickleness of our weather.

In England by far the largest amount of precipita-

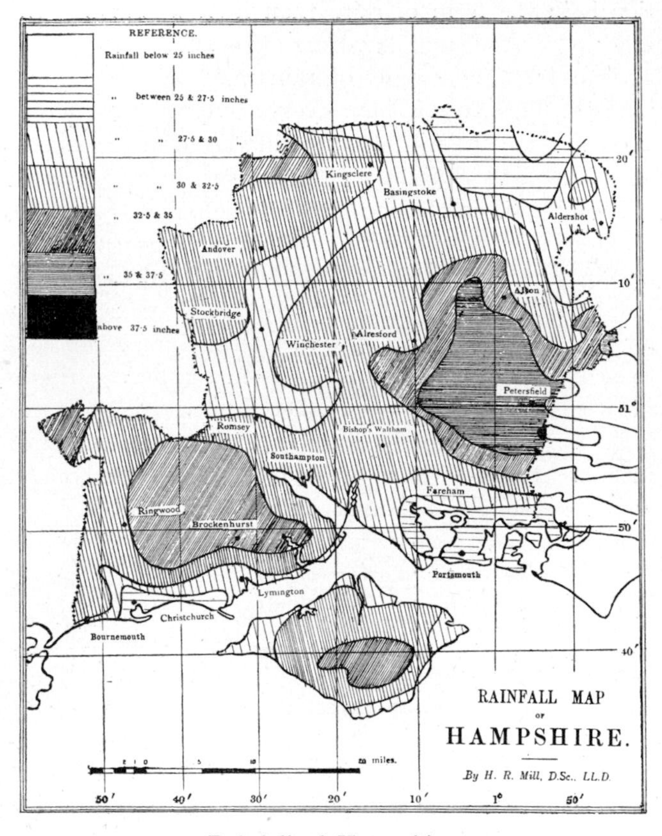

Rainfall of Hampshire

(By permission of Dr Mill and of the Controller of His Majesty's Stationery Office)

tion is in the form of rain, though snow and dew are other forms too, and have an important place also in agriculture. The causes of rain may be briefly summarised. The atmosphere everywhere holds within it a certain amount of moisture in the form of vapour, and if the air is warm it is able to contain more than if it is cool. When the air holds all the moisture possible at any given temperature it is said to be saturated, and if, when saturated, air is chilled, it gets rid of its moisture and rain falls. If, on the other hand, saturated air is warmed it becomes unsaturated and proceeds to acquire additional moisture from seas, lakes, rivers, marshes, etc., until it again becomes saturated at the higher temperature. If it is further heated, more moisture is picked up, and so on. When, therefore, air in motion is getting steadily warmer it becomes a drying wind; but when it is progressively cooled its course is marked by showers of rain.

There are several causes that result in air being cooled, but the chief one operating over land and sea is the well-known physical fact that if air passes into a space where it has opportunity to expand, temperature immediately falls. Such spaces occur at higher elevations where the air is less dense, and the pressure consequently less. On the other hand, the temperature of the air rises when it is, for any reason, crowded into a smaller space. Depressions such, for instance, as the central parts of cyclones, are therefore associated with rainfall, while over the high pressure areas associated with anticyclones the weather is almost invariably fine. The passage of a cyclone or anticyclone over any district therefore brings rain or drought independently of any influence of land masses. But the presence of land masses, especially if high land, exerts a powerful influence also on precipitation. In passing over hills the air is forced upwards into the colder region of lower pressure always existing at the higher altitudes, and the consequent fall of temperature often brings about rain. During the descent on the leeward side of the hill, the conditions are reversed, and this side is therefore drier than the other. As in England cyclonic conditions are associated with south-west winds, and as the chief elevations in the British Isles are in the west, in Ireland, Wales, and the Scottish Highlands, it will be seen that as we pass from west to east, the rainfall becomes less and less, varying from over 80 inches a year in Killarney, Glamorgan, and Cumberland (it actually reaches about 120 inches at Borrowdale) to 40 inches over Salisbury Plain, from 25 inches to 37½ inches over the greater part of Hampshire, down to under 20 in Cambridgeshire and parts of the East Coast. The general distribution of rainfall in Hampshire presents, therefore, no extreme feature.

The importance of climatic statistics has only been recognised of late years. The records of rainfall, temperature, sunshine, etc., are now systematically collected by an ever-increasing body of observers all over the country, and there is every hope that, as the work is extended, the general principles governing weather phenomena generally will emerge more and more clearly. Much information has been obtained as the result of the recent development of air navigation.

Rainfall is reckoned by the average number of inches of rain per year, but the actual fall in any one year may be very variable. From 1888 to 1905 there occurred a regular succession of one wet year followed by two dry years, 1903 being the wettest year of the period with an excess of 43 per cent. over the average, and 1870 the driest year, with a deficiency of 24 per cent. It is further to be observed that the whole country is passing through a cycle of years throughout which mild weather rules.

The general principles we have referred to are reflected more or less closely by the distribution of rainfall in Hampshire. If we were to follow the south-west wind inland from the coast we should pass over regions of increasing and decreasing rainfall more or less as we found ourselves to windward or leeward of the higher elevations. The Isle of Wight, with its high ridges, accentuates this "blanketing" effect, so that the region round Portsmouth Harbour is one of low rainfall (25 inches to 27.5 inches per annum). Over the New Forest a maximum of about 35 inches is reached, after which the rainfall diminishes, but in the elevated South Downs region all round Petersfield a decidedly higher maximum (37.5 inches) is attained.

The greater part of the Test valley is, as we should expect, a region of low precipitation (25 inches to 27.5 inches) but curiously enough the highest rainfall in the Test valley is at its southern end near Southampton

Water. The driest part of the county lies at its north-eastern extremity, in the low-lying Loddon valley.

How far surface characters, apart from elevation, influence rainfall is an interesting question. Thus in crossing the New Forest along our line (S.W. to N.E.) we rise from 25 inches to a maximum of over 32.5 inches, falling again as we leave the Forest, yet the elevation is nowhere over 400 feet, and the general level very much lower. It is probable that the increased rainfall recorded is due in part to the large area of woodland. Again, we may note that the greater rainfall occurs over the chalk or greensand, while the Tertiary belts, apart from the New Forest, receive decidedly less. The general distribution of rainfall in the county is given in the map on p. 69.

The driest month of the year in Hampshire is April. October is the wettest month, and from April to October the average rainfall regularly increases, decreasing again in an equally regular manner till April again is reached.

The prevailing wind over Hampshire, as over the British Isles generally, is west or south-west. The average temperatures over the county reflect the general mild character of the south of England. The northern region is cloudier and more humid than the southern, so that the total quantity of bright sunshine diminishes as we leave the coast proceeding northward. The sunniest part of the Channel coast is a strip extending westward from Beachy Head through Southampton to Lyme

Regis, and the whole coastal fringe of Hampshire, with the Solent and Spithead, as well as the Isle of Wight, is included in this maximum sunshine strip.

10. People. Population. Dialect

Hampshire has been peopled by human beings for vast ages. Long before the Isle of Wight became cut off from the mainland, and the Hampshire streams had carved out their present valleys, early races of mankind roamed over the Hampshire of that day. These men used flint implements, rudely chipped and shaped, which we find for the most part in the river gravels. We thus term these people the men of the River Drift—or men of the Palæolithic (*i.e.* Ancient Stone) Age.

Later—and probably after a considerable interval of time, though the question is still unsettled—a superior people came on the scene. They used implements of flint and bone, but of much more skilful workmanship. Many of these are beautifully wrought, finely shaped, and not merely chipped, but ground and polished. Of these people, whom we call the Neolithic or New Stone men, we find remains all over the chalk downs. They lived mostly on the upper levels—the only spots at that time at all open or possible for human habitation—they made clearings, which they gradually extended down the slopes, they pastured flocks and herds, and they used some primitive form of cultivation. Many of the huge earthworks, or "rings," which crown the ridges and summits of our Hampshire heights are their work.

We find their burial places—mounds of a long shape, called long barrows—and it was the people of this age, small of stature and with dolichocephalic (long and narrow) heads, who in Wiltshire erected Stonehenge and Avebury.

Then followed a more advanced race, larger of stature and with skulls of a rounder type (brachycephalic) than those of Neolithic man. These people knew the use of metals, making weapons and implements of bronze, from which fact they are called the men of the Bronze Age. They burnt their dead and buried the ashes in urns. Their burial mounds may be seen everywhere over the chalk uplands and the open heaths of the New Forest, round in shape, sometimes occurring singly, sometimes in groups, as at the Seven Barrows at Litchfield.

Then other races followed. Celtic tribes from Europe, moving ever westward in accordance with the great drift of population which has been in operation since the earliest ages of mankind, spread in successive waves over Britain. Two main streams of these folk have been distinguished—the Goidels or Gaelic Celts, who peopled Ireland and the Scottish Highlands ; and the Brythons (Britons) who followed later. The Brythons, who were users of iron implements, remained in occupation till somewhere near the time of Julius Cæsar. We speak of this period as the Early Iron or Celtic Age. Then lastly came Gaulish tribes from the Continent, such as the Belgae, the Atrebates, and the Segontiaci, and these and other tribes were in occupation in Hampshire at the time of the Roman invasion.

Compared with their predecessors the natives of Britain in Cæsar's time were a highly civilised folk. They were the first to form regular towns and villages. Agriculture was well developed, and many arts such as weaving, the making of pottery, and metal-working were practised by them. They made weapons and implements of iron, used metal coinage, and had chariots and horses for warfare. They engaged in regular commerce, the tin-trade in particular being of importance. The tin, obtained in Cornwall, was brought eastward over regular roads and tracks to the ports of Kent and Hampshire, whence it was carried oversea by Phœnician mariners.

Later waves of immigration belong to historical times. The Romans stamped their civilisation deeply on the county, providing it with a network of roads, and establishing towns or stations at many places, chief among them being Winchester (*Venta Belgarum*), Silchester (*Calleva Atrebatum*), Southampton (*Clausentum*), and Portchester (possibly *Portus Adurni*). Under them commerce and agriculture were greatly developed, and much of our county was covered with farms, the so-called Roman villas. Later, Roman Britain was to a considerable extent a Christian country. But, though they organised the country, the Romans never peopled it, and when, about A.D. 410, their legions were recalled, the people of the land were racially almost unaffected by the Roman occupation in spite of its long duration.

With the departure of the Romans, the country became again exposed to attack, and invaders poured in from all sides; Picts from the north, Scots from Ireland, and a mingling of Germanic tribes from over the North Sea—the people we speak of as Jutes, Angles, and Saxons. In Hampshire, two definite streams of these people can be traced. Jutish folk from Kent made their way hither by sea, and settled in the Isle of Wight, the Meon Valley, and the New Forest. The greater area, however, was occupied by the Gewissas, a mixed people of uncertain origin, who, with the Meonwara (the Jutes of the Meonland), between them formed the true stock from which our present Hampshire population has been derived. It was they who peopled and settled in the land, cleared the forests and thickets, drained the swamps, ploughed and sowed.

The period of the so-called Heptarchy, which lasted to about A.D. 800, was the critical period of the history of our land, for it saw the shaping of the system of land tenure referred to in the first chapter of this book, out of which practically all our laws and local institutions have sprung. There is scarcely a tiny hamlet or village in the land to-day whose name does not in some way or other bear the impress of this great period of construction.

In A.D. 829, Egbert, King of Wessex, consolidated and organised the Anglo-Saxon rule and became the first King of Angleland (England). Scarcely had he done so when the land was again imperilled, this time by the Northmen, or Danes as we often call them. For 200 years they threatened the land, and ultimately conquered it. Though large numbers settled here, they never became racially predominant. Born seafarers, they loved to establish themselves on the estuaries and creeks, and are hence spoken of as Vikings, or "creek-men" (from *vig* or *vik* a fjord or creek). In Hampshire, the site of a port for their vessels has been discovered at Longstock on the upper Test.

Saxo-Danish rule gave way in turn to Norman, and for some 200 years the Normans became the ruling race, infusing elements of culture, of disciplined thought, of art and learning. But though their influence on the ruling class, and through them on the country, was profound, the general stock of the people remained little altered. Indeed, it is not too much to say that the mingled Anglo-Saxon stock from which our Old English race was derived, exhibited from quite early days a remarkable power of absorbing and assimilating peoples of many different types, just as to-day the British Colonial people show the same power of retaining their racial characteristics while absorbing immigrants from practically every European land.

It is difficult now to trace present-day physical characteristics to their original source. The Gewissas were a fair-haired race, and the blonde type prevails in parts of Hampshire, as well as in Wilts and Dorset, but in the middle and north of the county the people are supposed to show a preponderance of the dark type, possibly due to Wendish ancestors. The Jutish type, with long oval skull and face, flat cheek-bones, and long nose, straight or aquiline, high under-jaw, and well-developed chin, is still to be noticed among the people of the Meon district.

Since the Norman period there has been no infusion of fresh races on a large scale. In early Plantagenet days Winchester had an important Jewish colony, with a ghetto and a synagogue of its own. In Tudor times various small settlements of Walloons were established in the county, and in 1567 a body of 100 were granted permission to settle at Southampton. In 1685, after the Revocation of the Edict of Nantes, French Huguenots took refuge in some number at Southampton, and thirty silk-looms were brought over here from Lille and Valenciennes. Of these Huguenot refugees, the most famous was Henri Portal, the founder of what has since become a great Hampshire family. It was he who started the paper industry at Laverstoke, and bank-note paper for the Bank of England is still made in the Laverstoke mills. At Southampton the French Protestant community still preserves some degree of continuity, and its members meet regularly for worship at the little historic church of God's House near the town quay.

The total population of Hampshire in 1911, excluding the Isle of Wight, was 862,393, being an increase since the former census of 145,229. The density of population is 583 per square mile, or nearly one person to the acre. England generally has a population of 618 to the square mile, and the greatest density of population is in Lancashire, where the number of persons is 2554 per square mile.

The density of population over the county varies enormously. Apart from military centres, the districts growing most rapidly in population are the large urban areas. The largest urban area, Portsmouth and Gosport, has a population of 263,000, and is growing at the rate of 2.15 per cent per annum. Southampton and Woolston, at present 138,000, grow at the rate of 2.72 per cent. per annum, and Bournemouth, now 78,000, shows an annual increase of 3.2 per cent. Eastleigh and Bishopstoke, owing to the removal thither in 1909 from Nine Elms, London, of the engine works of the L. and S.W. Railway, have a population now of 15,000, an increase annually of 6.3 per cent. The great military centres, Aldershot, Farnborough, Bordon, and Tidworth, all show large increases of population. One or two individual parishes only show a decline: thus, while there is practically no depopulation going on in the rural parts of the county, urban Hampshire is gaining ground rapidly.

The speech of our county is founded on the West Saxon dialect, which became recognised as the standard dialect of the Old English race through the literary labours of Alfred, and prevailed in his day from Hampshire and Berkshire as far north and west as Worcestershire and Gloucestershire. Recent investigation has shown that the vowel system of the West Saxon tongue was practically identical with that of the much earlier West Germanic parent tongue. Thus Hampshire speech is not in the proper sense of the word a dialect at all—rather can we see in it some of the main characteristics of the early English literary tongue.

11. Place-Names

The different stages of land occupation can be most readily followed by a study of the place-names now existing, nearly all of which have their origin in one or other of the early periods already mentioned. The earliest place-names are Celtic, and refer almost entirely to natural features of hill, wood, spring, and stream.

Most are water names, and among them are:—*An* or *Am*=a spring or stream, as Anton, Andover (=Andever), Amport, Ampfield, Ampner and Andwell. *Dover* or *Dever*=water, as in Andover, Micheldever, Candover, Durley, Overton, and Ower. *Ouse*, too (locally Uss), also=a stream, and occurs in Hurstbourne (locally Ussebourne), Owslebury (locally Usslebury), Oxenbourne (=Ousenbourn), and Ouse itself. The early Saxon name for Christchurch, Tweoxna (later Twynam) at the meeting-point of the two rivers Stour and Avon, is Twy-Ousena, or the Two Streams. The names Avon and Stour themselves are also of Celtic origin. *Ash* or *Ax* (also Esse)=water, occurs in Axford, Ash, Asholt, Ashley, Ashlet, etc., and *Wy* =water, in Wymering, and the two rivers Wey.

Of hill names we have *Pen*, a hill or head, in Inkpen on the Berkshire border, and *Cor*=a rounded hill, occurs in Corhampton.

Cwm or *combe*=a hollow, is frequent, as in Combe, Chilcombe, Compton, Combe Wood, Testcombe, Combe Bolton, Stancombe and elsewhere. *Bun*=end or

bottom, in Chewton Bunney, and Beckton Bunney, the deep river ravines in Christchurch Bay. *Pwl*=pool, in Polhampton, Polsden, Paulsgrove, etc.

Signs of the Roman occupation are mainly shown by the towns they founded, or the roads they constructed. The fortified towns are *chesters, e.g.* Winchester (Vinton, from Venta Belgarum), Portchester, and Silchester. From the roads we get *strat* or *streat* (=straight) as in Stratfieldsaye, Stratfield Turgis, and the Strattons. The Roman practice of marking distances along their roads by milestones may perhaps be preserved in Stoneham, referred to in Bede as Ad Lapidem.

The Saxon place-names tell us how the Saxon occupied the land and conquered in detail the formidable difficulties of soil, swamp, and thicket. In time the land became divided up more or less completely into estates or properties, the villeins or dwellers on each estate forming a separate and independent community under a lord or owner, from whom they held their portion of land, and to whom in return they owed service in some form. In a characteristic estate of this kind cultivation was on the open field system, the villeins grazed their animals in common on the pasture and stubble, cut their timber, and fed their pigs in the woodland and the waste. The cultivation was carefully regulated—the land was ploughed in acre strips, each strip being four rods or roods wide, and a furlong (=furrow long) or ploughing length (220 yds.) in extent. The width of the strip was measured by wooden rods, each 5½ yds. long, and a normal holding (viz. 30 strips), was called a "virgate" (Lat. *virga*), or a yard-land, both words having the same derivation and each meaning rod. The central area containing the dwellings of the community was usually "tyned"[1] or "girded" round for protective purposes by a fence of "girds" or rods, and thus came to be known as a *tun* or *worth* (*worth*=garth or yard). Sometimes these settlements were called *hams* (*ham*=home). The "tuns" or "worths" were the nuclei of most of our towns or villages, and hence the prevalence of these suffixes in local place-names of to-day. The map on p. 19 shows how the Saxon settled by the streams of our county, particularly the chalk streams, and in the Avon valley, along which "ton" and "worth" crowd one another. Out of nearly 100 "tons" and 14 "worths," about 80 "tons" are actually on the chalk area, 7 close to the Avon, and only 12 or 13 elsewhere, while of the 14 "worths" there is only one, Chilworth, not on the chalk area. This is in marked contrast to the "hams." Out of some 27 of these, 8 only are in the chalk area, 3 near the Avon, and 16 in the other districts.

The present-day parish boundaries indicate, generally speaking, the lines of ancient boundaries between one lord's lands and another's, and the areas often tend towards one of two types—blocks or strips—suggesting that the first-comers picked out the best land and made their boundaries to suit their own convenience, while later the mode of parcelling out was probably

[1] Both words, "tyne" and "gird," still exist in agricultural circles.

by royal grant or charter, and was thus more methodical. In many cases the areas form long narrow strips, roughly rectangular and of strangely exaggerated form, and nearly always running from one well-defined limit to another. Thus Ecchinswell and Sydmonton are two long parallel strips, over six miles long, but only half a mile wide, stretching from the Enborne river transversely across the ridge of the N. Downs, until they end at the Roman road, locally called Cæsar's Belt, running from Silchester to Sarum. Laverstoke is an equally extreme instance, stretching from the Roman road over the Upper Test Valley to the high ridge of Popham Beacons.[1] The strip principle can be traced in a very large number of cases. In the neighbourhood of streams the strips run across the valleys, being bounded by the stream where the latter is broad, but where it is narrow running across it and up the slopes on both sides. Such an arrangement is obviously chosen to give each strip its fair allowance of water and meadow land, arable, down, or dry pasture, wood and waste. South Tidworth, Shipton Bellinger, Thruxton, Quarley, and Grately, all form strips running directly athwart the hill slope; Monxton, Abbot's Ann, Upper Clatford, Goodworth Clatford, and Wherwell, are strips running across a stream.

Other Anglo-Saxon names indicate the nature of the settlement, its aspect, or some other natural or leading

[1] Laverstoke parish boundary on Popham ridge possibly marks an unrecognised Roman road from Popham Lane Corner to some point to the west.

feature. The most common suffixes of all are "ley" and "field," denoting open country, as Botley, Crawley, Winchfield, Froxfield, etc. The presence of buildings is shown by "stead" or "sted" as Medstead, Minstead, Silkstede; villages by "wick" or "wyke" as Wickham, Southwick, Wyke, and Rotherwick. Some were subsidiary in status—thus the "Bartons" and "Bereweekes" were the rickyards, *i.e.* storage places for the crops or "bear," *i.e.* bearing of a lord whose residence was elsewhere—as, for instance, Barton, Abbot's Barton, Barton Stacey.

Like the Celtic, many Anglo-Saxon place-names are connected with water or water features, *e.g.* "Stoke" "ford," "bridge," "wade," "bourne," "well," etc. The "fords" were natural crossings over shallow spots where a hard, gravelly bottom existed, so that a foothold was possible. Thus we get Droxford, Alresford, Charford, etc. The "wades" were deeper crossings, as at "The Wade" at Hayling Island, and Ringwood (Rin-wade in Domesday). The "stokes" or "stocks" were the more difficult crossings, marked out or otherwise protected by stakes. The best instance is Longstock, a long winding track across the peat marsh, and over the stream of the Test—also Laverstoke, etc. Basingstoke=the Stoke of the Basingas, *i.e.* the crossing maintained by them. The transition from a ford in early days to a bridge later is shown at Redbridge (=Reedbridge), which first occurs as Hreodford, (*i.e.* the ford among the reeds). There are at least 8 "stokes," 4 or 5 "wades," but only a few "bridges" in Hampshire.

Springs are denoted by "well," as Ecchinswell. The intermittent streams are "bournes" as Itchborne (=Itchenbourne), Somborne, etc.

Wood names are numerous. Clearings are "cleres," as Kingsclere, Burghclere, and Highclere; "wood" occurs in Woodhay (=Wood-hedge), Odiham (=woody-ham), etc; "holt," "hurst," "shaw," all meaning wood, in Linkenholt (=wood of limes), Brockenhurst (=badger's wood), and Bramshaw. Woods growing down the slopes of a hill are hanging woods, or "hangers," as in Oakhanger, and wild life is reflected in "Wolvesey" (=Wolves' Isle), Wolmer (=wolves' mere or wolves' pond), and Brockenhurst mentioned above. Wooded dells are "deans," as Bramdean and Dibden. The Celtic fortresses or entrenchments on the hill-tops the Saxons called "bury" (=burg, a fortress), *e.g.* Winklebury, Woolbury (=Worlbury), Danebury. Other names are patronymics, *i.e.* names indicating family or descent; among these are many ending in "-ing," as Basing, Eling, the settlements of the Basingas, Elingas, etc. Ellingham (=Ethelingsham), etc.

So complete was the Saxon occupation that the Danes, though much in evidence here, have given their names to relatively few places. *Wick*=creek, and *thorp* or throp = village, are their chief suffixes, *e.g.* Swanwick (Sweynes' wick) on the coast, but it is difficult to explain Ibthorp, Swanthorp, and Eastrop, occurring in the northern corner of the county. Norman names are not numerous, and are chiefly in the New Forest—*e.g.* Beaulieu and Purlieu, also Freemantle.

12. Agriculture

Agriculture in Hampshire, as elsewhere, depends on geological and climatic conditions, and these being very varied, the type of agriculture is also extremely varied. Historically, agriculture in our county has undergone great changes. As late as Tudor times the manorial system with its open fields and tillage in common obtained. On the borders of the manors stretched the Downs, over which large flocks were fed. Sheep-rearing for wool was indeed the great industry, and Hampshire a most important centre for English wool-production.

Of this open field system of cultivation no trace practically now remains, save here and there on sloping ground where the strips along which the soil was ploughed have left their mark on the surface of the land. The plough, passing continually lengthwise along the face of the hill, gradually worked out the side of the slope into terraces, with narrow banks called "balks" between them. Numerous traces of these "linchets" or "lynches," as they are termed, remain. Some are extremely ancient, others are medieval, others quite modern. They may be seen at Shawford, Easton, Twyford, Woolbury, and elsewhere.

With the wholesale depopulation caused by the visitation of the Black Death of 1349 and other years, came the gradual break up of this manorial system. Agriculture declined, the fields were enclosed, and cultivation by paid labour replaced that of common cultivation by the tenants of the manor. Nothing, however, has had more to do with changing the character of Hampshire agriculture, more especially over the central chalk plateau, than the introduction, between one hundred and two hundred years ago, of the turnip, and later, of the mangold. This rendered root-feeding possible during the winter instead of grazing, so that sheep are now fed over the arable land instead of merely over the Downs. This, together with the high prices obtainable for corn one hundred years ago, caused the pastures everywhere to be broken up, and corn and root-crops to be grown. The low price of corn since the repeal of the Corn Laws afterwards reversed the process, and much of the corn land was laid down again for pasture, though now again broken up.

The most characteristic agricultural district is naturally the central chalk area. All of this, practically, except the very highest ridges—which are covered with short nutritious springy turfs composed largely of sheep's fescue (*Festuca ovina*)—is overlain with soil, often of considerable depth, and good crops of all kinds are obtained. Much of it, particularly over the north, is excellent wheat land, and "seeds" (clover, sainfoin, lucerne, etc.) are largely produced. Most of the farming is mixed, *i.e.* part is arable, part pasture, so that sheep-grazing, the rearing of horned stock, and the raising of crops, are all carried on on the same farm. Soil conditions vary, and while in general the four-course rotation (2 corn crops, 1 roots, 1 seeds) is adopted, its exact nature is very diversified. On such a farm fertility is maintained by natural processes. The sheep grazing on the down land by day, and folded over roots by night, collect nitrogen from the down, thus continually enriching the arable and at the same time fattening upon it. Moreover, as leguminous plants—" seeds " so called—have the property of fixing atmospheric nitrogen, they thereby promote fertility. Considerable quantities of roots are of course grown for winter feeding. On such a farm below the down land the cultivated land occupies the upper levels ; on the lower levels are the grazing land and water meadows—meadows, that is, irrigated by artificial streams of water. In summer these produce excellent hay ; in winter, as the water rarely freezes, growth usually continues active, so that they yield plenty of feed, not only late in autumn, but early in the year, before growth on the upper levels has begun.

The so-called Woodlands—practically the Thames valley portion of the county—have quite a different character. The soil is largely a strong brown or grey loam, interspersed with thin sands overlying clays, water-logged, and unsuited for cultivation. Speaking generally, the soil is " cold " and the season more backward. It is therefore well adapted for woodland, and is dotted over with plantations. Cultivation over the whole county area, but more particularly the Woodlands, is greatly improved by dressing the land periodically with marl or chalk, and hence we find numerous chalk-pits over the chalk land, particularly along the edge where it meets the woodland district. " Marling " has been practised in Hampshire for centuries, and is regularly practised still, but less vigorously than formerly. The soil of the Woodlands will not carry sheep, but cattle are grazed. Some of it is good barley land, and good general crops are here and there grown.

The shrinkage of arable land and the development of grazing above referred to, have been specially marked over the Woodlands, where much of what was formerly wheat land has been laid down to permanent pasture. The fall in corn prices is not the only cause producing this result; the development of urban and residential districts, by creating a large and practically constant demand for milk, has rendered dairy-farming particularly profitable. Thus, though excellent cheese can be made, cheese-making as an industry is little practised in Hampshire. The development of permanent pasture has also curtailed the extent of sheep-farming. In fact, while during the last thirty years or so, horses have kept stationary, horned stock has increased 50 per cent, and cows in milk or in calf an equal amount, sheep have fallen off 28 per cent, and pigs, which twenty-five years ago were rapidly increasing, have again sunk practically to their former level.

No special breed of cattle is predominant throughout the county, but with sheep it is different. Originally the favourite breed was a white-faced horned variety, but special breeding, combined with winter root-feeding, has developed a type peculiar to Hampshire—the short wool Southdown, or "Hampshire Down" sheep, as it is termed. It is a large breed with black face and legs and gives a heavy clip of good quality wool, but the breed tends to diminish in numbers in favour of lighter kinds —Cheviots and mixed breeds. Enormous sheep fairs are held annually over the county. Weyhill Fair and Overton Fair are the best known, and buyers come from all parts to purchase Hampshire wool. Of pigs, the

Hampshire Down Sheep

favourite breed is the black Berkshire. The principal markets for stock are Basingstoke, Petersfield, Southampton, and Fareham.

The agriculture of the New Forest is different altogether from that of the rest of the county. The land is poor and thin, and often waterlogged. It will not bear sheep, but cattle of a small and hardy breed are grazed, large numbers of pigs are fed, and a distinct type of pony, the so-called Forest pony, is a special feature. The pigs too are of a distinct type, closely resembling the Large Black. They roam over the land, and feed largely on the beech-mast and acorns in the woods. The right of "pannage," *i.e.* the right to turn pigs out to feed in the woods, is an important right of the commoners in the Forest.

The New Forest pony is a semi-wild animal, small, light, and hardy, larger than the Shetland, and with an ample, though smaller, mane and tail. The mares are turned out, and breed in the Forest. Every year they are rounded-up, and the foals are branded according to the ownership of the dam they run with. The rounding-up of Forest ponies affords many an exciting scene, well figured in the familiar picture by Miss Lucy Kemp Welch. About a quarter of a century ago the New Forest pony was deteriorating, owing to the practice then prevalent, of selling off all the good foals and "suckers," and leaving only inferior stock to breed from. Now by the operations of the New Forest Pony Association, formed for the purpose, this has been checked, and by an infusion of new blood for breeding purposes, the breed has been greatly improved, so that yearling ponies readily fetch at least £2 a head more than they did fifteen years ago. The number of ponies in the New Forest is estimated at between three and four thousand. "Suckers" fetch £4 to £5, yearlings £6 to £7, and two-year-olds £10 to £12, according to quality. Regular sales are held at Brockenhurst and elsewhere. These prices (as those elsewhere in this book) are, of course, those prevailing before the war.

New Forest Ponies, near Lyndhurst

Many of the Forest holdings are quite small, and a good number of these were originally obtained by "squatters." The commoners proper have valuable and ancient rights of common, chief among them being:

Farm Yard with Ricks on "Staddles," Lee, near Romsey

(1) Mast-bote or pannage—the right to turn out pigs to feed.

(2) Pasture.

(3) Turbary or turf-cutting rights.

(4) Estovers or fire-bote—the right to dead wood for fuel.

Fern or bracken is largely cut and carted for litter, and formerly, during what are called the fence-months, cattle were not allowed to be pastured at large so that strays and intruders might be impounded.

13. Special Cultivations

Of several special cultivations carried on in Hampshire the chief is strawberry-growing, which is now an industry of importance. The reasons for its origin and success are the natural ones of soil, situation, and climate. Strawberries like a clayey, loamy soil, retentive without being cold, and such a soil they find to perfection on the Lower Tertiary fringe in the south. Here, on the sunniest belt of the county, they ripen early and thus hold the early market, maturing in regular succession according to locality. Among the first are those from Swanwick and the lower Hamble River area; Botley strawberries are generally a week later. The Kent strawberries are usually some days behind those of Botley, and with fruit and vegetables the early market is all important as regards prices.

The strawberry plants are grown in large fields, in rows wide enough apart for plough and harrow cultivation between them, small market-garden produce, such as autumn-sown and spring-transplanted onions being planted between the rows in the first year. The leading sorts are Royal Sovereign for the earlier, and Sir Joseph Paxton for the later crops. During the season (June to July), which lasts from three to six weeks according to weather conditions, strawberry-picking is the chief occupation of whole districts. The culture is a highly remunerative one, but the area has so much increased that the high prices of former days are now not so readily obtained.

With so perishable a fruit, marketing it rapidly and in perfect condition is a prime condition of success, and the strawberry train service is carefully organised. Picking is done early in the day, as far as possible, and the fruit placed in small baskets. Special trains, fitted with narrow shelves to receive the fruit, are provided, and are despatched several times a day both to London and the north. Locally there is also a large market, and great quantities find their way to Portsmouth, Southampton, and the Isle of Wight. Strawberry preserving is developing also as a dependent industry.

Strawberry culture is developing also in parts of the Woodland district, where the soil is of the same kind, though the season is much later. In certain places a considerable acreage of fir trees has been grubbed up to make room for these plants.

The relative importance of the strawberry culture in the three leading counties is shown by the following figures for 1914:—

	Acres
Kent	6365
Cambridgeshire	3356
Hampshire	2896

Apart from strawberries, fruit cultivation in Hampshire is relatively unimportant, although round Hedge End considerable quantities of raspberries are grown.

A much older-established culture in Hampshire is that of the hop, and hop-picking is one of the picturesque features of Hampshire rural life in the early autumn, as in Kent, dominating the whole countryside during the picking season. Hop-growing in former centuries was far more widespread than at present, but in England it is now essentially a local cultivation, for the hop plant depends much on soil and cultivation conditions, and

Watercress Beds at Alresford

is only profitable where these are well realised. It requires a soil retentive of moisture, cool, and somewhat heavy. It appears to do best where there is a mixture of formations, and the clay and clay marls overlying the so-called "malmstone" of the Upper Greensand suit it admirably, so that the hop-land follows the belt of Greensand all along the east of the county, from Prior's Dean and Selborne to Alton and Bentley. Though owing to foreign competition the area under hops over the whole of England has considerably decreased in recent years, in Hampshire it has held its own, and even slightly increased.

A familiar feature of the hop country is the oast-house, where the hops are dried. The drying is an important process, as the extent to which the bitter principle called lupuline, which gives the hop its value in "bittering" ale, is developed, depends largely on the skill employed in drying. Alton is the chief centre for hops.

Another special cultivation is watercress-growing. This is carried on extensively, particularly along the chalk streams. The temperature of the water issuing from the chalk springs is wonderfully uniform, viz. about 50° F., and the flow of warm water in February is very stimulating to the young shoots. At Alresford, Mapledurwell, and Old Basing in particular there are excellent and extensive watercress beds, but the culture is general along Hampshire streams.

A quite modern industry—tobacco culture—has been successfully carried out at Church Crookham. Commencing in 1911 with an experimental acre on a single farm, cultivation has been extended till the area was in 1914 about 30 acres, and several persons grew about an acre each. Crookham being the centre for all English-grown tobacco, special plant has been erected for curing, treating the leaves in heated chambers, packing, etc., and crops grown in other parts of the kingdom, notably in Scotland, North Wales, Norfolk, and Worcestershire, are sent here for curing. The leaves when gathered are stripped and sorted, then cured and dried. The curing is a delicate process and the final drying is done in specially constructed rooms heated by steam pipes to 120° F. Hampshire tobacco sells well, and there

Harvesting Tobacco, Church Crookham

is every prospect of tobacco culture developing into an important local industry.

Agriculture in Hampshire stands at a high level. Agricultural education receives special attention, and splendid work in this direction is being done by the County Farm Institute at Westley, near Winchester, which offers special facilities for agricultural education.

14. Industries and Manufactures

Owing to the absence of coal and metals, Hampshire, speaking generally, is not an industrial county, *i.e.* there is no definite manufacture which employs any large section of the population, and gives any marked industrial character to it as a whole. The county owes such industrial features as it possesses to its geographical position, and not to any advantages of soil or rock. Thus in 1911, out of 117,000 male residents, over ten years old, in active employment, 33,600 were engaged in agriculture, 31,500 in engineering, 10,000 in commercial and business pursuits, and no less than 38,000 in the carrying and transport of goods—forming the railway, dock, and mercantile marine class. The importance of trade-routes in determining the character and distribution of occupations and population in Hampshire is well illustrated by these figures.

The chief industrial centres are Portsmouth, Southampton, Eastleigh, and Basingstoke. At Portsmouth, industrial life centres round the Navy, and the town is practically an enormous ship-building and victualling-yard for that service. In the Dockyard every kind of ship-building and repairing is carried on, and industries such as flag-making, the manufacture of blocks and sheaves, and smith's work of every description. Every kind of ship's stores is provided, and there are large establishments for the supply of cordage, sails, and naval clothing. At Gosport, on the opposite side of Portsmouth Harbour, is the Clarence Victualling Yard, where every sort of food material for the Navy is either made or stored, the biscuit bakery being an important feature. Yacht-building is also carried on, particularly on the Gosport side, and on the slips further up the harbour. A special industry is the making of the finer qualities of sails for yachts.

At Southampton, on both sides of the Itchen, another large industrial population lies around the docks. Transhipment—loading and unloading goods—is the main work, and the needs of the port determine the large and varied industries carried on. Along the Woolston side—the district known as Itchen—ship-building yards, particularly Thorneycroft's, employ great numbers of men. Here torpedo and motor boats are built, and boats of every kind are constructed along the shore opposite the Docks. There are also large timber yards here. At Bursledon, too, on the Hamble, motor boats are made, and boat-building is a more or less important industry in a number of other places.

The commercial importance of Southampton as a port, and Portsmouth as a naval arsenal, have given a great impetus to railway and other forms of the carrying industry. The making of the railway to Southampton in 1840 began the development of Southampton as a port. In 1892, the L. and S.W. Railway acquired the Docks, and from that time development has been rapid, but of this we shall speak later.

The reaction of trade upon the railway industry has been responsible for the one industrial Hampshire centre which has markedly a character of its own, namely Eastleigh. Near the head of the Itchen estuary, where the lines to Southampton and Portsmouth diverge, it is a natural centre for railway construction works, and it has become, as it were, the Crewe of the L. and S.W.R. system. In 1909, the removal hither from Nine Elms of the engine works caused a further rapid development. In 1911 Eastleigh had a population of 15,247, of whom some 1500 were employed on railway work.

Although no other urban centre has a special industrial character, thriving industries are actively developing at various points in the county, dependent mainly on Hampshire agriculture. Foremost of these is Basingstoke. The rise of Basingstoke is instructive. The parent community was Basing, now Old Basing, a small village some two miles away, the headquarters of the De Port family in Norman days. Basingstoke (*i.e.* the staked ferry maintained over the Loddon by the Basingas), was then merely a convenient point for crossing the river. Lying at the flat head of the Test Valley to the south-west, and the valley of the Loddon to the north-east, with open land on either side, Basingstoke became a natural centre for population, as a point of intersection of the trade routes from London to the south-west, and from Southampton to the Midlands. In coaching days it developed as a coaching centre, in railway times it became an important railway junction, and the same causes have marked it out as a natural centre for mid or north Hampshire industries. Several firms manufacture agricultural implements, and more recently the great motor and other engine works of Thorneycroft's have been established here, employing as many as 1000 hands. Ironworks also exist at Andover, Winchester, Ringwood, and elsewhere.

Some of the countryside occupations are occasional

Railway Works, Eastleigh: the Brass-finishers' Shop

and seasonal rather than permanent callings, such as hurdle-making, thatching, etc. Hurdle-making, one of the most ancient of rural industries, is general all over the wooded parts of the county. Hurdles, before the war, fetched from 8s. to 9s. a dozen, and they take an hour to make. It is hard work, and the poor price makes it difficult to earn much at the work. Thatching is declining, partly owing to the cost of straw, but more to the difficulty of getting men skilled in the art. Wheat straw is used for general thatching, for ricks, and for potato clumps. The best thatched roof, however, is made of the reed (*Arundo Phragmites*) which grows freely in the river swamps, but in many farms nowadays corrugated iron roofs are superseding the old thatch. For ornamental thatching purposes ling or heather is frequently employed.

With the numerous rapid streams flowing through the county, we should expect milling to be widespread, and it is so. There are numerous mills on the streams; some grind corn, others are paper-mills. The grinding industry inland, however, is a decadent one. It tends to concentrate at the ports, owing to the influx of foreign corn, and to decline elsewhere. Large mills exist at Southampton and Fareham, but there are also still many inland, as at Winchester, Bishopstoke, Bossington, Droxford, and elsewhere.

Paper-mills were at one time more numerous than they are now. The paper-mills formerly at Alton have now ceased to exist, and those at Romsey have also declined. The most important factory of this nature is that of bank-note paper for the Bank of England, still carried on at Laverstoke, as has already been mentioned.

Timber, both native and imported, is sawn in large quantities at various mills along the rivers. Large sales of New Forest timber are held every year, and much of it finds its way to the saw-mills at Totton and Southampton. There are large mills also at Durley. The smaller mills along the streams in many cases carry on quite a definite industry. The harder woods, mainly beech, are rough sawn to make brush-backs and similar articles, which are sent away to factories in distant parts of England.

In the woodland areas, particularly in the New Forest, the charcoal-burner still pursues his occupation much as he did in the traditional days of William Rufus. The charcoal was formerly much in demand for iron smelting, but the decay of that industry locally has caused it to dwindle. Brick earth abounds, particularly along the clays of the Eocene, and bricks are made at many places. Fancy pottery and terracotta are made at Fareham, and there is a large tannery at Romsey.

With the centralisation of industry in modern times, and the increased facilities for transit, many Hampshire industries have now disappeared. For instance, with the great production of wool in the county, we should have expected to find weaving and spinning, as also leather working, well established. Such industries once existed, and for centuries Southampton, Winchester, Alton, Basingstoke, Andover, and other places, all carried on some textile industry or other. The Flemish weavers who settled at Southampton in Tudor times wove cloth and woollen goods, and worsteds were for centuries made at Winchester. Alton made serges, druggets, and barragons; Fordingbridge gloves. Now the wool and skins are all sent away for manufacture.

Two other important industries have also entirely disappeared, viz., salt manufacture and iron-smelting. The "salterns," or salt-works along the coast, particularly on the low swampy shores from Hurst to Lymington, existed from immemorial antiquity, and are referred to in numerous old deeds and records. But the superior salt made in Cheshire, combined with cheap and easy transport, proved their ruin. The last of the Lymington salt-works disappeared in 1865, and thus "the commerce which eighty years before had paid £50,000 a year into the Exchequer, lined the shore with a busy population, and covered the Channel with merchantmen, has now totally ceased."

Another extinct industry which was of considerable importance up to the middle of the eighteenth century is that of iron-smelting. Artificial dams were erected to work the great hammers needed to beat out the slag, forming what are still called hammer ponds. One of these is Sowley Pond, 100 acres in area, 3 miles east of Lymington, formed to work the great hammer of Sowley, and another the Hammerpond at Wakeners or Waggoners Wells, near Bramshott. Ironstone was regularly quarried at Hengistbury Head, and the smelting done at Sowley with charcoal from the Forest and limestone from the Isle of Wight as a flux. Hence the importance of the charcoal-burning industry of earlier days. The use of pit coal in the iron centres of the North ultimately did away with Hampshire iron-smelting, but it lasted till the latter end of the eighteenth century. At that period the district all round Lymington was a busy spot. At Buckler's Hard, on Beaulieu river, several vessels of Nelson's Trafalgar fleet were built by the famous shipwright, Adams.

15. Fishing

The fishing grounds of the British Isles are the most productive in the world, far exceeding in total product the other two considerable grounds, namely, the waters round Japan, and in the neighbourhood of Newfoundland. Moreover, the North Sea fishery—for this is the most important of western Europe, owing to the warm shallow sea affording abundance of food—is the best organised and most efficiently worked. Beyond one marine league from the shore—the "three-mile limit"—the sea is open to all nations but, in the North Sea, the English from the east coast ports preponderate over every other nation, both in numbers of men employed, and in the average amount caught, for hundreds of steam trawlers (of which other nations have very few) stay out weeks at a time, passing the fish on to smaller vessels for landing as it is caught. The chief fish is the herring, of which so many have been caught that the fish remaining in the sea have become seriously diminished in quantity. International arrangements have been made for close seasons and close areas, so that this fish may not become extinct. Mackerel, cod, plaice, and soles are also numerous. The south coast of England is much less productive, and has only a very few steam trawlers, while the west coast is poorer still.

On the Hampshire coast, Portsmouth, Hamble and Warsash, and Christchurch are the chief centres of the fishing industry. Portsmouth produces soles and plaice by trawling, herrings and mackerel by drift nets, sprats by seine nets, escallops and oysters by dredging, lobsters by pots and trawls, and periwinkles by hand picking. Christchurch produces salmon, and also soles, flounders, herrings, prawns, crabs, and lobsters. Emsworth has oyster beds. The most important part of the fishing industry centres, however, at Hamble and Warsash, which are practically the headquarters of the crab and lobster trade in England. The shellfish are not caught in the neighbourhood, but fishing smacks collect from down the Channel as far as the west coast of England and Ireland, the vessels being fitted with wells to enable the catch to reach their destination alive. There are commodious ponds at both Warsash and Hamble in which they can be stored and kept alive, and the shellfish industry is not merely confined to home markets, but is an extensive Continental trade. Indeed, for a very long period the Hamble river has been a centre for this industry. The monks of Beaulieu and Netley centuries ago had oyster beds in the river, and oysters used to be sent from here inland to the monasteries at Winchester and elsewhere. Prawn fishing by push nets is also carried on at many points of the coast, *e.g.*, Calshot.

Hampshire has been traditionally a favourite haunt of lovers of the rod. Precentor Wulfstan in the tenth century, speaking of the stream of water brought into Winchester by Bishop Aethelwold's enterprise, says, "Dulcia piscosae flumina traxit aquae." Izaak

Walton, who was a great lover of Hampshire, and died at Winchester, stated that Hampshire exceeds all England for swift, shallow, clear brooks and stores of trout. Charles Kingsley haunted the Hampshire streams, and has left memories at Eversley, Whitchurch, Avington, and elsewhere.

Fishing Hut and Eel Trap on the Test, near Longstock

Salmon, trout, grayling, eels, pike, and coarse fish generally are all taken, but trout-fishing is the fishing *par excellence* of Hampshire—the Test and Itchen rank among the most famous trout streams of England. Nearly all the water is carefully preserved, and there are trout hatcheries at various places. The chief fishing reaches of the Test are from Whitchurch to Romsey (below Romsey the Test may be considered rather as a salmon than as a trout river) and on the Itchen from Ovington to Shawford. Grayling occur in the Test as far as Fullerton, and in the Itchen as far as Shawford. Salmon enter a number of Hampshire streams. They are netted from February to July in the famous "run" or narrow channel at the entrance to the Avon, near Mudeford. The Test below Romsey is an excellent stretch of salmon water, and salmon may often be seen in the river from Romsey bridge. There are a few in the Beaulieu river. In the Itchen, salmon can only ascend as far as Woodmill.

Eels are caught plentifully. "Stockbridge eels" are famed. The Avon is the best river for pike and coarse fish generally, Ringwood and Fordingbridge being good centres. Pike also are plentiful in the Loddon and other waters of the north of the county.

16. Shipping and Trade

Hampshire has two great centres of sea trade and business—Portsmouth, the Naval arsenal and dockyard, and Southampton, the great commercial port. Before these had attained such predominant importance, the shipping industry was active at many points along the coast. Now Southampton forms the converging point of nearly all the lines of trade and sea-borne traffic to the almost entire exclusion of other places. Bournemouth has no trade whatever by sea. Havant and Fareham have a small trade with shallow-draught vessels, mainly in flour, timber, and coal. At Christchurch and Lymington trade has dwindled to small dimensions. Portchester, at the back of Portsmouth

Harbour, once a busy point of military landing and embarkation, is now so no longer.

Portsmouth Harbour has been a centre of maritime activity for nearly 2000 years. Here the Romans established the westernmost of the fortified stations from which they controlled what was called the "Litus Saxonicum" or Saxon shore—that part of the eastern and southern coast which, even in Roman days, Viking or other North Sea pirates were in the habit of raiding and plundering. Roman Portchester was strongly defended with walls, and its Roman masonry, 10 feet thick, still stands. For the shallow-draught vessels of Norman days the innermost parts of the harbour were most advantageous, but from King John's time onwards, as the draught of vessels steadily increased, docks with deeper water became necessary, and a dock town began to grow on Portsea Island and the mud flats at the harbour mouth. Thus Portsmouth waxed, and by Henry VIII.'s time waning Portchester was already becoming obsolete. Since that date, the development of Portsmouth has been continuous. Its convenient position, the extent and depth of anchorage in the harbour—where it is said that the whole British Navy could lie—its tidal facilities, and above all its security, protected by the narrow harbour mouth and the flats and shallows of Spithead on which strong forts have been erected, have combined to mark out Portsmouth as the great naval centre of England. Henry VIII.'s reign first saw it rise to importance. In Stuart times it received a great impulse. In the naval wars of

Napoleonic and Georgian times, it played a preponderating part. Now its importance is still more definitely emphasised.

A great amount of general maritime trade centres in Portsmouth (which for this purpose includes Gosport on the opposite side of the harbour), for it is a great place of import for all manufactured and raw materials needed for the vast quantity of naval stores which the dockyard supplies. But, speaking generally, Portsmouth is not an exporting centre. Her commercial docks, the outer and inner Camber, form a considerable bend behind Point Battery, but their small extent relatively to the dockyard shows the comparatively small importance of the place as a port proper.

As a commercial port Southampton occupies a conspicuous place. Its geographical position marks it out as a natural world port, lying as it does in the middle of the Channel coast, within easy reach of London, and with the great " hinterland " of the Midlands and Wales to draw commerce from. But over and above this, its protected waters, and the special tidal conditions already mentioned which Southampton Water enjoys, give it natural advantages that no other English port can claim. For all this, Southampton as a port has had its periods of prosperity and decline.

In Norman days Southampton first became of importance, forming one end of the Anglo-Norman " bridge " from Hampshire to the mouth of the Seine. In Plantagenet periods it carried on a great trade, not only with France, but also with Genoa and Venice,

H.M.S. *Victory* in Portsmouth Harbour

(*From a Drawing by J. M. Whichelo*)

exporting wool and importing wines, oil, silks, and Eastern wares generally. The Genoese and Venetian carracks or galleys obtained permission in 1378 to make Southampton their port of destination, as it saved the long Channel voyage up to London—just for the same reason that the big liners of the present day have made it their port of call.

The prohibition of export of wool in Henry VIII.'s reign stopped the Levant trade, and the port fell on evil days. At the time of the Armada, Southampton was unable to provide even two ships and a pinnace for national defence. The Atlantic trade and the Newfoundland fisheries which had sprung up as the result of colonisation in Tudor and Stuart times, greatly restored its prosperity, however, but the place remained of minor importance till the beginning of the nineteenth century, when an attempt was made to improve the port so that it might rival Falmouth and Plymouth. The proximity of London gave it a great advantage, but the first real impetus came in 1830, when a railway scheme was first mooted. The line was completed in sections, and ultimately in 1840 the whole was in operation.

The dock schemes had been in hand since 1803, but in 1836 large docks were actively commenced, and in 1843 they were opened. The mud lands at the Itchen mouth were to be reclaimed, and the docks excavated on them. Continued progress marked the successive stages of reclamation and growth carried into execution then and since, and the port became a moderately good one for small vessels, but the docks were not a commercial success. In 1892, however, the L. and S.W. Railway Company bought the docks, enlarged them, and constructed new ones, at the same time improving the communications with the metropolis. The White Star Line then moved its headquarters from Liverpool to Southampton, and from this time the port has increased very rapidly in size and importance. In 1910 it stood fourth on the list of British ports for tonnage of ships, the figures being :—

	Tonnage Entered.	Tonnage Cleared.
London . .	12,154,162	8,999,635
Liverpool . .	7,588,653	6,697,512
Cardiff . .	5,523,895	8,562,764
Southampton .	4,342,459	4,192,713
Plymouth . .	1,492,531	1,351,949

The value of the exports, which in 1845, when the docks and railways were first opened, stood at £1,475,000, had in 1880 reached £9,306,326. The population has increased in the same way. In 1831 it was 19,324; in 1881, 59,916; and in 1911, 119,012; thus just doubling in the last thirty years.

Notable among the imports of the place are the large quantities of meat from South America and the Colonies, and other cold storage articles. The installation for cold storage is indeed the largest in Europe; it accommodates hundreds of tons of beef and mutton, millions of eggs, and large quantities of poultry, fish, butter, and game.

Southampton as a port is one of the best equipped in the world. The Empress Dock has 26 feet of water at low tide, and is the only dock in Great Britain where deep-water lading and discharging berths can be reached by the largest vessels at any time of night and

The White Star Liner *Olympic*

day irrespective of the state of the tide. There are 35 miles of railway line around and about the docks, thus giving direct access to every railway in the country. Ships can be discharged or loaded throughout the night, as the whole is brilliantly lighted by electricity. The facilities not only for entry at all states of the tide, but for rapid loading and unloading, have been the determining factor in the rise of Southampton, and have put it on a level with Liverpool and New York. The port has been extensively used for embarkation of troops, both in the South African and the Great European War.

The supreme jurisdiction of the port was at one time far wider than at present. In 1384 the whole coast from Hurst to Langston was included within its authority. The jurisdiction over so wide an area caused frequent disputes, but the Admiralty rights of Southampton over Portsmouth were acknowledged as late as 1835, when they were abolished.

Nothing shows more conclusively the extent to which Southampton has grown of recent years than the list of important shipping firms which now use the port. The Royal Mail, White Star, Union Castle, Elder Dempster, Cunard, British and Irish Steam Packet Co., City of Cork Steam Packet Co., Clyde Shipping Co., American Line, and Rotterdam Lloyd are among the number, as well as the L. and S.W.R., which has a large fleet of vessels. Before the war the Hamburg Amerika, Hamburg S. Amerika, Nord-Deutscher Lloyd, and other huge German liners were a regular feature of Southampton.

17. History of the County

The Romans, who occupied Hampshire from about A.D. 50 onwards, constructed roads and raised walled towns, as at Winchester and Silchester, besides establishing forts and stations along their lines of road. The recall of the legions left the county a prey to the Anglo-Saxons, and Jutes and Gewissas peopled and gradually reclaimed it. Shut off as it was from the east by the dense forest belt which covered the south of England, it received no call to Christianity from Augustine's mission (A.D. 597), and it was not till A.D. 634 that Birinus, the monk, who had been sent on a mission to Britain by Pope Honorius, brought Hampshire the Gospel message. Kynegils, the then King of Wessex, became a convert, and at Birinus' instance, founded a monastery at Winchester, and hither, towards the close of the seventh century, Bishop Haedda transferred the Bishopric. In 687 Bishop Wilfrid of York, the evangelist of Sussex, converted the Jutes in Meonland to Christianity. Kingdom warred with kingdom until Egbert, King of Wessex, made himself overlord, and was crowned King of Angleland at Winchester A.D. 829. Thus Hampshire, the centre of Wessex, became the cradle of English rule as well, with Winchester as the capital.

For a century or so Hampshire history was one with English history, and though as years developed the position of London gave the latter increasing advantage, it was not until some centuries later that it became the undisputed capital of England. Egbert, Aethelwulf and his four sons—of whom the last and greatest was Alfred—Edward the Elder, Athelstan, Edgar, these are all great alike in Hampshire and in English history, and all made Winchester their capital. Most of them were buried in Winchester, and at Winchester Cathedral their memories, if not their very bones, will still be found preserved, together with those of Kynegils and his son Kenwalh, the first two Christian kings of Wessex. It was at Winchester that Alfred reigned, and consolidated his rule; it was here that he attracted that rare circle of scholars whose literary labours he directed, the outcome of which were the *English Chronicle* and Alfred's own translations into the vernacular. His and succeeding reigns, moreover, saw the establishment of monasteries at Winchester, the new Minster, founded by Alfred; St Mary's Abbey by Alswitha, his queen, and Romsey by their daughter, Edith; and later Wherwell by Edgar's widow, Elfrida. Then early in the eleventh century the Danes gained the upper hand, and Winchester became the centre of the great Anglo-Danish empire, under Cnut. The traditional scene of Cnut's rebuke to his courtiers is on the beach by the Town Quay at Southampton, and it was above the high altar of Winchester that Cnut hung up his crown in token of humility. He died in 1035, and was buried in Winchester.

With the advent of Norman rule in 1066, Hampshire still retained its importance. William was crowned both in London and at Winchester, and regularly held his court here at Easter. It was at Winchester that Curfew was promulgated, and Domesday Book compiled. Rufus was killed in the New Forest, and Henry I. succeeded in 1100. Robert, his elder brother, the Crusader, attacked him, but at Alton the brothers met, and Henry I. bought him off and was left to reign in peace.

During all this period, Portchester had been very notable as a port, chiefly for military purposes. Henry I. erected a castle here and founded an abbey, which was moved fifteen years later to Swanwick. He also built

The Great Hall, Winchester Castle

a Priory at St Denys, Southampton. Stephen's weak reign and the civil war saw Hampshire devastated. Castles were erected in various parts of the county; Stephen's brother, Henry of Blois, Bishop of Winchester, building those at Wolvesey, Winchester, and Merdon. Others, some of them earlier, were erected at Winchester, Odiham, Southampton, and Christchurch. The two castles at Winchester were held by opposing factions, the royal castle for Matilda, and the Bishop's castle for Stephen. Henry II.'s reign saw peace restored, and various castles destroyed, among them Merdon. Odiham, as a royal castle, remained.

With the loss of Norman interests which followed John's reign of misrule, Winchester declined in importance, and during the Baron's War the place was twice besieged and suffered heavily. Henry III. rebuilt the Castle Hall, a noble building still standing, and here some of the earliest representative Parliaments were held.

The medieval days saw the end of the great pilgrimages, and the development of the great fairs. The pilgrimage centre of Hampshire was Winchester, where St Swithun's shrine was in high repute. The pilgrims' route was from Southampton, by St Cross, to St Swithun's; then on by Headbourn Worthy church, where an early Saxon rood on the outer western wall would be visited, and so by Alresford and Alton to Farnham. Then a halt would be made at the Cistercian Abbey of Waverley, whence they went by Guildford to St Thomas's shrine at Canterbury. The track followed by the pilgrims can still be traced out in places over the Down.

The great fairs were those of Winchester and Weyhill. Both attracted enormous crowds—that at Winchester was held for sixteen days on St Giles's Hill, during which time all trading, except at the fair, was prohibited in the city and for ten miles round. The profits from this fair went to the Bishop, but the borough of Andover received those from Weyhill Fair. Winchester Fair is now all but extinct; that of Weyhill still remains as a great sheep fair, though with nothing like the importance of medieval days.

Hampshire reached a high degree of prosperity in Edward I.'s reign. The Hampshire wool clip was of great importance, and Winchester was the "staple" town where all wool sales for the county had to be held. Southampton was the port of export, and both prospered highly. It was the wool sale, indeed, which caused the great development of the fair at Winchester. Edward III.'s reign saw Southampton develop also as a military port, and in 1346 Edward and the Black Prince sailed hence for France on the Crecy expedition. Edward's foreign policy, however, caused the ruin of Hampshire—he removed the wool staple from Winchester to Calais, to encourage the trade with Flanders. Winchester and Southampton rapidly declined, and the Black Death completed their ruin. From that day the inland towns of Hampshire sank and dwindled, and thenceforward the development of the county has been almost purely maritime.

The wars with France made the coast vulnerable to attacks, in the course of which Southampton, Portsmouth, and other places suffered. In Edward III.'s reign Southampton's sea defences were consequently much strengthened, and naval and military activity continued to develop. It was from here that Henry V. sailed on his famous Agincourt expedition. Henry VIII.'s foreign policy gave the seaboard increased importance. Southampton built great ships for his navy, and Portsmouth was by this time a strongly fortified naval base. Henry also erected defences all along the shore—at Cowes, Southsea Castle, Netley Castle, Calshot, and Hurst—the three last built from the spoils of the Cistercian abbeys at Netley, and from Beaulieu, dissolved a few years

Alton Church

before. Southampton had by this time decayed, and Hampshire took but little part in the Armada episode.

James I.'s reign witnessed the grant of a charter to Romsey, and the disgraceful condemnation at Winchester of Sir Walter Raleigh. In this reign also the *Mayflower* sailed to New England from Southampton. By this time Portsmouth had become the war port, and from hence the Duke of Buckingham's forces sailed to attack La Rochelle.

Then came the Civil War. In this Hampshire played a vigorous part. Portsmouth was seized by the Royalists, but was attacked and captured by the Roundheads. This had important consequences, as the Roundheads were enabled to hold the coast fortresses, and the loss of the sea ports—so important even then was sea-power—had great weight in determining the ultimate result. The Roundheads then attacked and plundered Winchester, but the Royalists recovered, and drove their opponents from that city and the centre of the county, though they were unable to dislodge them from the coast.

Towards the end of 1643 the Marquis of Winchester, who had fortified Basing House and held it for the King, was strongly besieged, and a fierce fight in Alton ended in a defeat of the Royalists, Colonel Boles being driven to take refuge in Alton church, where he and his little band perished, fighting bravely to the last. The bullet-marks may still be seen on the door and pillars of the church. In 1644 a more serious disaster befel the Royalists, when Sir William Waller defeated their army marching to relieve the Roundhead pressure. This heavy blow decided the Royalist cause in Hampshire, and Cromwell marched south after Naseby, besieging and taking Winchester and Basing, the latter of which had kept up a heroic resistance for nearly three years. Winchester Castle, Wolvesey Castle, and the fortress at Basing were "slighted," *i.e.* dismantled. The later episodes of the Civil War are concerned with the flight of the King from Hampton Court. He reached Titchfield, whence he sailed over to the Isle of Wight, expecting protection from Colonel Hammond, the governor. Colonel Hammond, however, kept him prisoner, and after a year's imprisonment at Carisbrook he was sent

Basing Church

over to Hurst Castle. Here he was detained about a week, and thence he passed by way of Romsey, Winchester, and Farnham to Windsor. Seven weeks later he was beheaded.

Portsmouth continued to grow during Charles II.'s reign and after, and for 150 years Hampshire history largely centres round that town. In James II.'s reign the ripples of Monmouth's rebellion in the West disturbed

Hampshire life, and at Winchester Judge Jeffreys opened the Bloody Assize by condemning Dame Alice Lisle to be burnt at the stake within twenty-four hours, a cruel sentence, for which the Judge only after earnest entreaty consented to substitute execution. The aged lady, who bore herself with extreme dignity, was executed at Winchester. She is buried at Ellingham.

Later Hampshire history—apart from Portsmouth and its dominating influence in naval matters in the Napoleonic Wars—is mainly the story of the development of the traffic routes, first by coach and then by rail. The coaching days brought prosperity to the inland towns—Alton, Basing, Petersfield, Alresford, Ringwood, Odiham, and Andover. Then came the railways—at first resisted, then encouraged. The village posting-houses and inns all declined. Towns left out of the railway scheme, as Odiham, and the country districts generally speaking, suffered as the favoured towns grew. In recent days the cycle, the motor, and the desire for country residence have done a good deal to redress the balance, and town and village hostelries are once more prosperous.

Later developments inland have been practically all military. After the Crimean War, the waste and open land near Aldershot was made the centre of a great permanent military encampment. Aldershot is now an important urban centre, and Farnborough, its near neighbour, is also developing fast. Then came the establishment of Bordon Camp in Wolmer Forest, and Tidworth Camp near Shipton Bellinger. Further changes, due to the great war, are beyond our scope.

Meanwhile the great increase of traffic facilities has made Southampton a world port of prime importance, which promises, as far as can be foreseen, to increase still further. Southampton and Portsmouth together seem destined to be more and more the seats of a large industrial maritime population, and the day may come when the mud flats of Southampton Water, not only at its head, but also along both its shores, will be lined with wharves and sheds.

18. Antiquities

Hampshire has preserved a varied record of practically every era of human occupation from early Palaeolithic times to the present. Many of these remain above the soil, often practically undisturbed, among them being burial mounds, earthworks of every kind, "rings," dykes and trenches, ancient cultivation-ridges, and early trackways. Many have escaped destruction by the plough, others the worm and the plough have even preserved for us. Stone and bronze weapons, coins, foundations of buildings, Roman pavements and relics of all kinds, pottery and metal work, a Jutish burial ground—these are but some among many treasures which have been covered up by earth and thus protected from destruction.

Palaeolithic man has left behind him, buried in the river gravels, the rude stone implements he fashioned in early days, but no traces of his work above ground exist. Neolithic man, on the other hand, has left his mark permanently over a wide area; the long barrows and most of the great circular earthworks capping the hills are his work. In Hampshire they form a wonderful series, in the main aligned on the two great ridges which cross the county from north-west to south-east. Generally speaking, they have a common family resemblance—a ridge thrown up on the slope looks down into a deep ditch or fosse, the whole running around the hill-top and enclosing a large area. Nor is the arrangement of these "rings" fortuitous; they occur at intervals, usually having the next within sight, and are joined by tracks which keep as far as possible to the tops of the ridges. From long-continued ages of use and weathering, these often bear the character of trenches rather than trackways.

What was the purpose of these rings? Examination of the evidence points to prolonged rather than to temporary occupation. The trackways from camp to camp are too permanent and too deeply worn to have been for occasional use only, and the most probable explanation is that they were the earliest settlements of Neolithic man, though succeeding races in many cases no doubt used and developed them. Frequently, indeed almost invariably, near the rings the hill slopes above the present cultivation-levels exhibit shallow ridges, showing where the camp dweller carried out his primitive agriculture in the limited open area or natural clearing around the settlement. Below this level came

The Itchen and St Catherine's Hill, Winchester

the thick continuous hedgerows of natural origin to which we have already referred, which originally formed the upper edge of the primitive forest and now mark the cultivation limit.

These "camps" vary from the simple form of St Catherine's Hill, Winchester, with its single fosse and vallum, to the highly complex multiple series of trenches and defensive entrance-works of Danebury. Among the most characteristic are Woolbury (or Worlbury) overlooking Stockbridge, Tidbury Ring at Bullington, Beacon Hill in Burghclere parish, Bury Hill near Andover, and Old Winchester Hill near Meonstoke. The largest local camp is Walbury, just overlooking Combe, which for geographical purposes is really Hampshire, although since 1894 it has been administratively included in Berkshire.

Long barrows exist, among other places, at Old Winchester Hill, Danebury, Chilbolton Down, the Giants' Graves at Charlton near Fordingbridge, Whitsbury, etc.

The Bronze Age men, who followed the Neolithic, doubtless made use of these camps and enlarged and extended their protective lines, but their chief remains are the Round Barrows. These occur in groups at Litchfield (seven), Clarendon Hill, Tidworth (nine), Popham Beacons, the Devil's Jumps near Privett, and elsewhere. Groups of round barrows have recently been destroyed at Danebury and at Winklebury, and doubtless they were much more abundant in earlier days than at present.

The barrows, both long and round, are sepulchral, but their contents vary very much in character. The long barrows contain skeletons—usually in groups—of the earlier Neolithic peoples, the round barrows show single interments of the broader-skulled Bronze Age man. The dead, especially in the long barrows, are often buried in a sitting posture—in the round barrows traces of cremation are frequently found, and the ashes of the dead are placed in urns of pottery. Bones of animals, pottery, and personal ornaments may occur in all, and in the round barrows bronze weapons and food vessels.

Of rarer occurrence and of particular interest are the so-called "promontory" or "peninsular" camps, of which several excellent examples occur in Hampshire. In these, water formed a natural defence round the greater part of the area, and the narrow strip or neck of land giving access to it was protected by a dyke or series of earthworks. Their age is uncertain. The most characteristic inland example occurs near Bransbury, where an area of about 60 acres, lying just above the level of the waters, has been defended from attack on the eastern side by a curving bank, 800 yards long, known as the Andyke. Pyott's Hill near Basing is an instance of a similar kind, and Hengistbury Hill has been converted into a sea-shore promontory camp by the so-called Double Dykes, cut across the narrow isthmus.

The best example of the so-called British villages is the group of pit-dwellings at Hurstbourne. These were nine in number, circular, and from 12 to 13 feet in diameter, with sloping passages leading down to them, the floors being 4 feet below the surface, and roughly paved with flints. Portions of millstones used for grinding corn, bones, pottery, and a large number of "pot boiler" stones were found, but no metal articles, thus indicating that these dwellings were of very remote antiquity.

Of Roman times numerous traces remain. Roman walls still stand at Silchester and Portchester, and the walls round a considerable part of Winchester not only clearly outline the limits of the Roman city, but actually stand on the Roman foundations. The great Roman roads may still be tracked for miles along many parts of the county, and the plough and spade have revealed foundation courses of Roman farm buildings with pottery and implements, tesselated pavements, etc. in many parts of the county. A Roman villa was recently excavated at Stroud, near Petersfield, and Roman altars, stones with Roman inscriptions, and other articles too numerous to mention have also from time to time been unearthed.

Of these antiquities, the one far surpassing all others in extent and interest is the Romano-British city of Silchester. Here once stood a British settlement which in later Romano-British days was protected by a wall—not foursquare as original Roman walls invariably were, but following the irregular course of the earlier British vallum. At the meeting-point of two Roman arteries of traffic, Silchester had its day of importance. Later, the traffic flowed along different lines. The opening up of the Thames valley formed a route westward from London to the north of Silchester, and the more natural route from London to Winchester and Salisbury through Basingstoke outweighed even the advantages afforded by the Roman road. Thus traffic westward flowed to the north and south; Silchester was passed by, and Reading sprang up where the junction of the Thames and Kennet formed a natural place for crossing. Away from any channel of intercourse, Silchester gradually atrophied and decayed. Bit by bit its stones were used for building material, leaving the great walls standing, and to this happy circumstance we owe its preservation to-day.

The area within the walls has been systematically excavated, the results carefully plotted, objects worthy of preservation removed for safe-keeping to the Reading Museum, and the soil afterwards replaced, so that the visitor will see little of interest actually on the surface. Most interesting of all the finds were the foundations of a Romano-British church, with a small piece of mosaic pavement at the eastern end, on which the altar stood, and a narthex or small porch at the western extremity. Outside the walls at the north-east corner is the small but extremely interesting amphitheatre.

The objects found at Silchester are very numerous, and a splendid collection of them exists in the Reading Museum, where almost everything illustrative of Roman life in Britain is shown. Coins and medallions, some with Christian emblems engraved on them, articles of use and adornment, glass, pottery, the implements used in trade and in the shops, even the toys of Romano-British children, are all to be seen here.

The other Roman towns, Winchester, Southampton, and Portchester, have yielded much of interest, but of quite minor importance compared with Silchester. Clausentum, or Roman Southampton, does not appear to have been on a large scale—it stood on a peninsula to the east of the Itchen, near Bitterne. The site is practically open land still. Stones with inscriptions have been found here, but not very many. Indeed, Roman Hampshire has left behind it singularly few inscriptions. Of Roman camps, so-called, there are several in the county, but very few of them are really Roman. One Roman camp exists at Ashley, half a mile north of the Winchester-Sarum Road. Egbury (? Vindomis) is thought also to be Roman, and there are some others.

Of antiquities of post-Roman date the Jutish burying-place at Droxford in the Meon Valley is the most important. We have already seen how a Jutish tribe, the Meonwara, settled on the shore and made their way up the Titchfield river, until they peopled the Meon Valley. In cutting the railway from Fareham to Alton, a burial-place of these folk was discovered. One skeleton of enormous size, no less than 8 feet long, with a sword by its side to match, was also found.

Of considerable interest, but of uncertain date, is the so-called Danish ship, the keel of which still lies buried in Hamble mud, off Bursledon, and can be seen at very low tides. Portions of it are preserved in the Westgate Museum at Winchester. There is a vivid account in the *English Chronicle,* of a fierce fight between King Alfred's navy and six "aescas" or Danish long-ships, somewhere along Southampton Water. Only one of the invaders got away. Three were driven ashore on the scene of the encounter, and two had to be beached elsewhere. The captured crews were led to Winchester, where King Alfred ordered them to be hanged.

19. Architecture—(*a*) Ecclesiastical

A preliminary word on the various styles of English architecture is necessary before we consider the churches and other important buildings of our county.

Pre-Norman or, as it is usually, though with no great certainty termed, Saxon building in England was the work of early craftsmen with an imperfect knowledge of stone construction, who commonly used rough rubble walls, no buttresses, small semicircular or triangular arches, and square towers with what is termed "long-and-short work" at the quoins or corners. It survives almost solely in portions of small churches.

The Norman Conquest started a widespread building of massive churches and castles in the Continental style called Romanesque, which in England has got the name of "Norman." They had walls of great thickness, semicircular vaults, round-headed doors and windows, and massive square towers.

From 1150 to 1200 the building became lighter, the arches pointed, and there was perfected the science of vaulting, by which the weight is brought upon piers and buttresses. This method of building, the "Gothic," originated from the endeavour to cover the widest and loftiest areas with the greatest economy of stone. The first English Gothic, called "Early English," from about 1180 to 1250, is characterised by slender piers (commonly of marble), lofty pointed vaults, and long, narrow, lancet-headed windows. After 1250 the windows became broader, divided up, and ornamented by patterns of tracery, while in the vault the ribs were multiplied. The greatest elegance of English Gothic was reached from 1260 to 1290, at which date English sculpture was at its highest, and art in painting, coloured glass making, and general craftsmanship at its zenith.

About 1300 the structure of stone buildings began to be overlaid with ornament, the window tracery and vault ribs were of intricate patterns, the pinnacles and spires loaded with crocket and ornament. This latter style is known as "Decorated," and came to an end about 1350 with the Black Death, which stopped all building for a time.

With the changed conditions of life the type of building changed. With curious uniformity and quickness the style called "Perpendicular"—which is unknown abroad—developed after 1360 in all parts of England and lasted with scarcely any change up to 1520. As its name implies, it is characterised by the perpendicular arrangement of the tracery and panels on walls and in windows, and it is also distinguished by the flattened arches and the square arrangement of the mouldings over them, by the elaborate vault-traceries (especially fan-vaulting), and by the use of flat roofs and towers without spires.

The medieval styles in England ended with the dissolution of the monasteries (1530–1540), for the Reformation checked the building of churches. There succeeded the building of manor houses, in which the style called "Tudor" arose—distinguished by flat-headed windows, level ceilings, and panelled rooms. The ornaments of classical style were introduced under the influences of Renaissance sculpture and distinguish the "Jacobean" style, so called after James I. About this time the professional architect arose. Hitherto, building had been entirely in the hands of the builder and the craftsman.

Hampshire churches fall into two classes—the Collegiate or Monastic churches, and the parish churches and chapelries. Of these latter there are few which from their size or architectural character can be described as stately, but the monastic churches are among the noblest in the land.

The churches of the county as a class are ancient. Pre-Norman work—pre-Conquest work that is—exists in many places. There is, however, no example of a complete Saxon church, such as Bradford-on-Avon can show; the Saxon work is always present with work of later times.

Along the Meon Valley, with its memories of Wilfrid of York, several extremely ancient churches exist. Corhampton, with its pilaster strips on nave and chancel, "long and short work," and ancient sanctuary stone or "frith-stool," is one of the best. Warnford church possesses a Saxon dial, and an inscription records

Breamore Church
(*South Transept Arch, with Anglo-Saxon Inscription*)

that the earlier church on the same site was built by Bishop Wilfrid himself. At the opposite corner of the county, at Breamore, near Fordingbridge, is a still more interesting church. The Saxon tower and south transept are practically perfect, and the nave, chancel, and transepts show the characteristic pilaster strips admirably. In the porch is an ancient crucifixion

Romsey Abbey
(*Abbess's Door and Anglo-Saxon Rood*)

group, eminently Saxon in method and treatment. A similar group, greatly mutilated, exists at Headbourn Worthy, and a far more beautiful one, perhaps of this period, on the outer wall of the south transept of Romsey Abbey. Saxon work is also found at Boarhunt, Tichborne, Warblington, and elsewhere. Similar in character, but of post-Conquest date, is Chilcombe church near Winchester.

The great impulse to Norman came when Bishop Walkelyn, the first Norman Bishop of Winchester, pulled down the existing Saxon cathedral of Aethelwold, and began the present building. Cruciform, with a square tower, with nave, triforium, and clerestory of somewhat heavy but truly dignified Norman character, it must have been a revelation to its first beholders. Bishop Godfrey de Lacy, in the twelfth century, extended it eastward, and William of Wykeham transformed most of it, giving to the interior the lighter and more graceful beauty of Perpendicular arch and tracery. The original Norman character can be seen in the transepts, and good examples of practically every later style can be well studied in the building. Christchurch Priory came next in point of time, with its beautiful Norman turret, diaper moulding, and interlaced arches. At Romsey, the Saxon abbey was rebuilt somewhat later as a Norman Transitional church, and at St Cross, which is very similar to Romsey, a little later still. Both have beautiful work in choir and transept, and the interlacing arch-work seen at Christchurch is repeated here more extensively.

The impulse first given by Bishop Walkelyn is seen in Hampshire churches generally. Brockenhurst, Fawley, Droxford, Tichborne, Compton, East Meon, Portchester, Winchfield, Hurstbourne Priors, Sydmonton, Burghclere, and St Maurice, Winchester, among many others, show excellent examples of Norman work. Particularly beautiful are the doorways, which exhibit a gradual change from rough tooling with the hatchet to beautiful chiselling. At St Michael's, Southampton, is a fine Norman tower, encased in later work. A

North Transept, Christchurch Priory Church

particularly perfect specimen of a Norman church is Nately Scures near Basingstoke.

The later Norman churches all show finer work—fuller detail and more delicate chiselling, closer bedding of the stone courses one on another, and the tendency to the pointed arch. Alton, Easton, the three churches of St Bartholomew, St Peter, and St John at Winchester,

Norman Work in Choir and North Transept, Romsey Abbey

Warnford, Crondall, Kingsclere, and Goodworth Clatford, are examples.

The change from Norman to Transition and Transition

to Early English came naturally as the masons acquired more and more mastery over their materials. The mechanics of building construction and design were in fact not fully understood in Norman times. As time went on the builder learnt more and more how to balance his material and dispose his masses—hence the light shafting and graceful spring of the Early English arches and arcading. Barton Stacey, in particular, shows this light spring of the arches admirably. There was much rebuilding of churches in Hampshire in the early thirteenth century, and Early English work exists in abundance.

The best examples of the Perpendicular style exist in Winchester Cathedral. The nave, transformed by William of Wykeham, is of perfect conception, and in the beauty and perfection of the reredos and of Wykeham's chantry Perpendicular work reaches its zenith. Christchurch Priory church, in nave and chantries, exhibits the same type of beauty. Basing and Basingstoke are among the few good parish churches in this style. The two chapels at Winchester College and the beautiful cloister work reflect the same spirit and character.

With the advent of the Tudor period, English church architecture declined. The side screens of Winchester Cathedral choir show how it passed away, and how the foreign artist with Renaissance ideas brought from abroad replaced the native craftsman. To turn from the strength and vivacity of the carving of the miserere seats of Christchurch to the facile mediocrity of Gardiner's chantry at Winchester reveals how completely the joy of the craftsman in his handicraft had by the sixteenth century passed away.

Of the interiors of the Hampshire churches, the fonts

The Font, Winchester Cathedral (12th century)

are for the most part Norman or Early English, and as a rule reflect much the same general character. Four are of special interest, the four black limestone fonts, at Winchester Cathedral, St Mary Bourne, East Meon, and St Michael's, Southampton. The carving is extremely quaint and rude. The material from which they were made was brought from Belgium at the end of the twelfth century.

There are but few good church towers, and few spires. Barton Stacey has a fine tower. Micheldever, Basing, and Basingstoke are also noticeable. Hurstbourne

Netley Abbey

Tarrant has a small tower covered with shingles. Some good examples of flint-built churches exist, as at Soberton, Privett, and St Mary's, Portsea.

We have already mentioned the monastic churches. The influence of the monasteries on early church and social life was great. The earliest monasteries and nunneries were of the Benedictine Order, such as

St Swithun's Priory at Winchester, Hyde Abbey, and Christchurch. The nunneries, St Mary's Abbey, Romsey, and Wherwell, followed the Benedictine rule. Portchester Priory, afterwards moved to Swanwick, was a Priory of Augustinian Canons, as were also Selborne Priory, and Mottisfont. The Cluniacs were not directly represented, but of Cistercian houses, an offshoot from Cluny, Hampshire possessed two noble monasteries, Beaulieu, founded by King John in 1204, and Netley by Henry III. in 1239. The neighbouring monasteries of Quarr, Isle of Wight, and Waverley near Farnham, were also Cistercian. Titchfield Abbey, founded in 1222, was Premonstratensian. Beaulieu and Netley are to-day noble ruins, but that is all; the merest vestige of Hyde Abbey remains; the others, apart from Winchester Cathedral, Romsey Abbey Church, and Christchurch Priory Church, have all passed away. Beaulieu parish church of to-day is the old Priory refectory, and lies north and south instead of east and west.

20. Architecture—(*b*) Military

Military defensive architecture may be said to be well represented in Hampshire. Strongholds had existed here, as we have seen, in Roman times. Alfred the Great defended the county with "burhs," but, apart from Portchester, Silchester, and Wolvesey walls at Winchester, nothing now stands above ground of earlier date than the Norman.

In Norman days, strong "royal" castles were erected at Winchester, Southampton, Portchester, and Odiham, and there was also a Norman castle at Christchurch

Bargate, Southampton, from the North

(then called Twynam). The Norman castles both at Winchester and Southampton were built on elevated ground in a corner of the town. At Southampton there were strong defences on the north or landward side, of which parts, *e.g.* the Bargate still remain. How far the defences round the other side were complete is uncertain, but they were certainly inadequate, for in 1337 an assault was made by sea on the town by the French, and Southampton was sacked. The seaward defences were then greatly strengthened, and much remains in excellent preservation to the present day. A tidal moat ran north and south by what is now Canal Walk, and east and west in front of the Bargate, the beautiful arcaded portion along the west, now called the Arcades, was erected, and, thus completed, the walls of Southampton contained twenty-nine towers and seven principal gates, of which four still stand. God's House tower projected eastward, so as to enable defenders to enfilade an enemy attacking from that side. Water Gate led direct to the Town Quay, and Westgate to the western shore. The scheme of defence of a medieval city can be well studied in Southampton.

Winchester Castle and defences equally have their visible records still. The Normans found Winchester already walled, but they improved its defences. The original stronghold of Saxon Winchester, as we have seen, had been Wolvesey, which occupied the south-eastern corner of the city, its magnificent wall—much of it still standing—defending that quarter. Later Saxon kings relinquished Wolvesey, and it became the residence of the bishop. How William I. strengthened the city, erecting his castle at the upper angle to the south-west, and how Henry of Blois, the bishop, converted his residence into a stronghold and built another castle without royal warrant at Merdon, has been already related.

Henry III., who was born at Winchester, rebuilt parts of the castle; and the noble Great Hall, which he then erected, is the finest building of its kind in the south of England. The city in this reign stood more than one siege, and the defences were accordingly strengthened. Of the five gates only two now stand intact, one a remarkably fine specimen of defensive work of Edwardian times. Over the other gate the little parish church of St Swithun is perched, an arrangement not infrequent in medieval days, when ground space within the area of the walls had to be carefully economised.

Portchester Castle, erected by Henry I. on the site of the Roman fort, still exists, though nothing more than a ruin. It was used in the Napoleonic wars to intern French prisoners of war. Odiham and Christchurch Castles are both ruins.

Later military works belong to Tudor and Stuart times. Of Henry VIII.'s castles Calshot and Hurst still remain. Calshot Castle, with its round tower, acts as sentinel at the entrance to Southampton Water, and, like Hurst Castle, is very strongly fortified. Of Basing House the extensive ruins alone are to be seen.

Speaking generally, while military architecture is not a leading feature of Hampshire, its development illustrates how geographical conditions reflected themselves in the military works; how the Normans, secure by sea, fortified themselves on the landward side;

how the Plantagenets needed protective works against home and foreign foe alike; and how under the Tudors sea defences were greatly strengthened, while the castles inland were converted into peaceful country residences, which, save for the disturbing eddies of the Civil War, they have since remained.

21. Architecture—(*c*) Domestic

Hampshire is a county of noble mansions and splendid country seats, of manor houses of great beauty and interest. Its cottages, too, in a humbler way, can claim distinction. Half-timbered, daub-built, and with thatch roofs they form a pleasant and old-world feature of the rural landscape.

As security from foreign invader and local robber increased, the baronial and manorial residences lost their defensive character, and houses more commodious and open replaced them. Not many Hampshire residences recall outwardly their earlier history. Lord Montagu's house at Beaulieu, however, built where the Abbot's residence once stood, with the Abbey ruins as a background and the defensive moat seaward, built in Napoleonic days as a guard against attack by sea, tells its own story. Here and there a Tudor or Jacobean mansion remains but little altered from its original form, as The Vyne near Basingstoke, and the splendid Jacobean building at Bramshill. More frequently it is Georgian influence that is reflected, as at Stratton, or Broadlands near Romsey. The manor houses are a numerous series—too numerous indeed to be mentioned in detail here. Some of them still retain traces of the moats by which, in the insecure medieval times, they were protected. There is an extremely interesting Manor House at Wymering, and Bramley Old Manor House has an excellent half-timbered front.

Hampshire town architecture dates from very early times. At Christchurch one of the earliest existing chimneys, dating from Norman times, reminds us how the Normans, who extinguished domestic fires by the curfew, taught the Saxon how to deal with the smoke as well. In few places can town geography be so well studied as in Southampton—the ancient houses and narrow ways dating from at least Norman times clustered behind the Water Gate, the great warehouses, the splendid Tudor mansion Tudor House, the change from medieval to Georgian, the flowing out of the town for residential purposes to the open country on the north, the reclaiming of the shores for mercantile purposes on the seaward side—all these are of note and interest.

In this respect Winchester is less illustrative, and old Portsmouth, though full of interest, is mainly Georgian in type. The method of grouping at Basingstoke, Alton, Alresford, and Petersfield, where one long street largely predominates and the houses are aligned along the old coaching road, tells the story of their development in a different but characteristic way.

The Hampshire old-world rural cottage is a diminishing type to-day, indeed perhaps before long a vanishing one. The typical rural cottage is built wholly of daub or half-timbered, the roof is of thatch, often reaching nearly to the ground, and the whole is set back from the road with a well-stocked garden in front. It is often a picture of great beauty—externally, that is;

Thatched Cottages, near Lyndhurst

for within, the charming and picturesque cottage is only too often cramped, dark, and poorly ventilated.

Good daub or "dob," as it usually is called, is a mixture of clay and chalk material, and is not now so readily procurable as formerly. Straw for thatching is more expensive, and skilful thatchers to carry out the work are fewer, so that these cottages when past repair are more and more being replaced by hideous modern brick cottages, usually tiled, sometimes slated. Flint is largely used, particularly where the clay-with-flints overspreads the county, and here and there, as in the Selborne districts, cottages are built of stone. Chalk also, as has already been stated, is made use of here and there, generally in combination with other material.

Chalk-built Farm Buildings, near Prior's Dean

Not less characteristic are the old daub walls which in some places abound. The material will not bear soaking with water, and consequently the top of the wall is roofed over either with thatch or with tiling. Older walls are daub throughout—later ones are often a mixture. The foundation courses and corner work are generally of brick or flint, the body being of daub.

The large timber-built, thatched barns, often of great charm of form and colour, nowadays tend to be

Thatched Daub Wall, Pitt, near Winchester

replaced by structures of metal work in which corrugated iron plays a leading part, and just as early man passed from flint in weapons to bronze and iron, so rural Hampshire to-day is passing alike from mud and thatch and hand implements to iron for construction, and machinery for labour.

22. Communications

The earliest existing roads of Hampshire were of the simplest type, and can in many cases still be followed along the ridge of the chalk upland. Very possibly—particularly where they descended into the valleys or crossed streams—some of them followed tracks made originally by wild animals—for, whether by air, by land, or by water, animals love to keep to an accustomed path. We have seen how along the ridges of the downland the "camps" of Neolithic man and his successors are aligned. It is quite easy to follow the ancient trackways, still clearly to be discerned, that connect camp with camp; as for instance from far beyond Walbury, by Beacon Hill and Ladle Hill, right on to Winklebury; or the other tracks which lead by Danebury to Woolbury, and from Old Winchester to Butser Hill—probably parts of a much larger trackway which led from Stonehenge to the Sussex Downs.

But all ancient trackways are not of this character. Some avoid the camps, as for instance the famous Harroway, which led originally from the west country past Stonehenge, past Weyhill and Hurstbourne to

Farnham and beyond. Its name is thought to mean the Hoar (*i.e.* ancient) way, and it is part of an ancient road leading from Mounts Bay in Cornwall right on to Dover. It crossed the Roman road, constructed later from Winchester to Silchester, near the village of Worting, and eastward of this point is known as the Pack Lane. Another ancient track, the origin of which is unknown, is the Lunway, connecting Woolbury with Swarraton. The New Forest also is covered with ancient tracks in every direction. A proof of the antiquity of these tracks is that they do not touch the modern towns and villages—the conditions which dictated the positions of these not being in operation when these early pathways were first trodden out.

Gradually, as what we may call the sense of the community grew, routes began to be opened up for tribal purposes. We have already spoken of the tin trade and the much-discussed tradition that tin was brought through Hampshire to Lepe on the Solent, and across by a passage then fordable to the Isle of Wight, and thence exported. Whether this was so or not does not greatly matter. The point is that such trade routes to and from the coast, and elsewhere across the country, were certainly in existence when the Romans came.

The Roman occupation brought fundamental changes. The Roman looked at the country as a whole, and opened up through communications throughout the length and breadth of the land. His roads were primarily designed to secure military control, and linked up one fortified station with another. As a rule they ran in straight lines from point to point, though deviations were not unknown. From Winchester at least five roads radiated —to Silchester (*Calleva Atrebatum*), to Cirencester

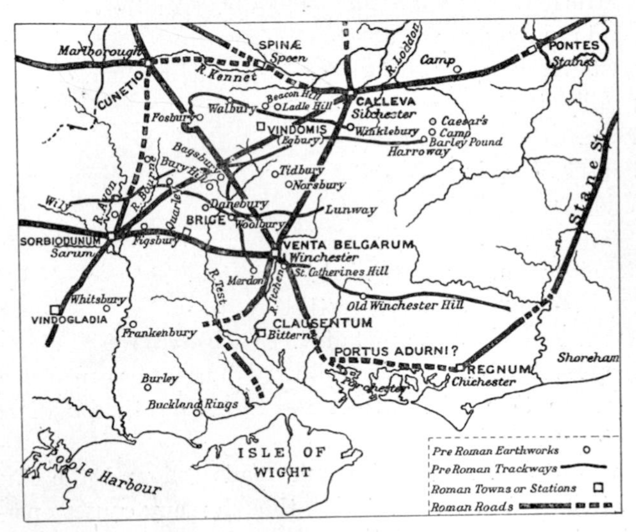

Roman and Pre-Roman Roads and Settlements in Hampshire

(*Durocornovium*) by way of Fosbury and Marlborough (*Cunetio*), to old Sarum (*Sorbiodunum*), to Southampton (*Clausentum*), and to Portchester (*Portus Adurni*). The last named is interesting, as at its Winchester end it followed a curved route for about a mile, taking the line of the earlier British trackway, which then led from Winchester to Old Winchester Hill.

A Roman road of great importance led from London through Silchester direct to Old Sarum and the west country. This was the Port Way. It crossed the Winchester-Cirencester road practically at right angles, a little north of present-day Andover. Another principal road ran roughly parallel to the coast from Southampton past Warblington to Chichester, and another can be readily tracked from Dibden Purlieu, near Hythe, to Lepe. Recently a road has been traced from Otterbourne, crossing the Test at Nursling, and so on to Wimborne.

The Roman roads were scientifically constructed on a definite plan. They varied in width and were metalled with stone " setts " where these were procurable, much as modern roads are metalled. They were raised above the level of the surrounding land, and hence the common title High Street for the main thoroughfare of town or village.

Saxon and medieval trunk roads followed the line of the great Roman arteries, though many causes operated to produce deviations from them. From Roman times onward for many centuries, it is not too much to say that roads were more or less left to themselves. There was no general policy followed in maintaining them in repair. When a road became badly worn, traffic followed new and parallel tracks on either side, and so the modern roads are frequently found to take a line parallel to the old Roman one. Moreover, the steep gradients necessitated by the straight course of the Roman roads, and local difficulties of swamp or river, further operated to make wide deviations necessary.

An interesting example of this can be seen in following the Roman road from Winchester to Cirencester. For seven miles out of Winchester the present highway takes the old Roman line up and down over the high ridges in a straight line. Near Barton Stacey, however, it deviates sharply to the west through Wherwell, where it crosses the river Test by a bridge, and so goes on to Andover. The original road exists, however, beyond this point of deviation as a well-defined track, forming for some short distance part of the road to Barton Stacey, till it loses itself later in the marshes of Bransbury Common. Crossing the Micheldever and Test rivers in two fords, it becomes recognisable again as a track over the land and so on to the north-west. Curiously enough the site of the Roman road is still clearly defined locally, for the spot where the L. and S.W. Railway line passes over it is indicated by a bridge, which is a conspicuous landmark as we look northwards across Bransbury Common. The explanation of the divergence lies in the marshes of this latter area, for all the roads near it are regularly flooded, even nowadays, in spring and winter. The new road followed the more natural route, and linked up Winchester directly with Andover and the fertile Anton valley.

But roads were not merely made to connect town with town. Many of them had their origin as lines for the conveyance of particular goods or traffic. Such is the origin of several of the tracks to which the word "way" still clings. Besides the Harroway and Lunway already discussed, we have Saltways, Oxways, Maultways, etc., and, most picturesque perhaps of all, the Pilgrims' Way. The Saltways led direct inland from the "Salterns" or Saltings on the coast. In medieval, as in early and late Saxon times, before the days of winter feeding for stock, large numbers of animals had to be killed and salted down for winter. Hence the salt industry was extremely active, and the Saltways came into existence. The word Maultway is believed tc be derived from a word meaning "sheep." The movements of cattle are indeed responsible for many existing tracks, and the steep side lanes in particular often found dropping direct into the valleys mark old tracks made by cattle coming down to water.

In medieval times modes of conveyance were varied. Wheel traffic was only to a limited extent in vogue, owing to the bad surface of the roads. Travellers rode on horseback, ladies were conveyed in litters and on pillions, and goods were taken on horseback or muleback. Long trains of sumpter mules or horses followed one another—often under armed escort because of the danger of robbers—and, when the weather was favourable, heavy goods were placed on rude sledges and dragged along. The wear caused by traffic, intensified by rain, frost, and wind, deepened the ruts, particularly in chalk and sand districts, so that in certain places we find the chalk downs scarred deep into remarkable narrow gulleys. The best instances of this are to be seen near Winchester, on the downs south and east of the city. Looked at from the cathedral tower these tracks can be seen in bunches spreading out fan-wise over the upland. The tendency for tracks to sink or cut their way down can be well seen in the Selborne district, and the "sunk roads" of this neighbourhood were specially commented on by Gilbert White.

The development of coaches in later Stuart days directed attention to the roads and by the early part of the eighteenth century their defective condition had become so serious a hindrance to communication, that in many cases private individuals subscribed money, repaired the roads, and erected toll-gates upon them, taking tolls from those passing through. Violent opposition was aroused by this, and Acts of Parliament, known as the Turnpike Acts, were passed to regulate them. Thus a new and improved system of roads gradually came into existence.

The first highway in Hampshire to become "turn-piked" by law was part of the London Road from Sheet to Portsmouth. This was in 1710. Commissioners were appointed for controlling the road and regulating the tolls. The effect of this was to cause existing roads to be greatly improved, and new roads to be made. In fifty years' time fourteen Highway Trusts were created.

In 1840 the first railway was opened, and this lowered the tolls so seriously that for some years roads again fell into much less efficient condition. Changes in administration were found necessary, and roads became disturnpiked, tolls were abolished, Highway Boards were formed, and the cost of upkeep placed on the various parishes. Ultimately, in 1888, the control of the chief roads was placed in the hands of the County Council. Such roads are technically termed main roads.

Deep Cutting, Butser Hill, Portsmouth Road

For other roads the municipal boroughs, rural, or urban district councils are responsible.

The modern road as we know it thus dates almost entirely from the eighteenth century, but the surface was generally speaking poor till the time of M'Adam, at the beginning of the nineteenth century, whose great principle was that roads should not only be of proper gradient, but be made of road-metal of uniform size—(instead of stones indiscriminately large and small)—

well rolled in and properly contoured or cambered. In quite recent days the introduction of fast motor traffic has made it more necessary to eliminate dust, and the best roads now are surfaced with material containing tar in some form.

Military requirements have lately played an important part in road development. The establishment of great permanent military centres or camps at Bordon and on Salisbury Plain some twenty years ago made good new roads necessary, and the great war has added to their number.

Before we leave the subject of roads, we may pause to note a point of interest in connection with the more ancient highways. Here and there as we pass along them may be seen widish stretches of open land fringing the road, known technically as "waste." These were a regular feature of medieval roads, and not only allowed the traveller an alternative if the ordinary track had become impassable, but acted as a protection against highway robbers. By Statute of Westminster in Henry III.'s reign, all trees and bush growth had to be removed a bowshot from the road, to prevent robbers from lurking and suddenly attacking travellers. In later times, by Act of Parliament, the manor lords have been allowed to enclose the waste up to a certain distance from the middle of the road. Here and there, however, the waste still remains unenclosed, and where this is so we may say almost certainly that the road is an ancient one.

The first canal work of importance in Hampshire was

the attempted canalisation of the Itchen by Godfrey de Lucy, Bishop of Winchester, in the twelfth century. To keep a sufficient volume of water, he built a dam across the river Alre at Old Alresford, forming he lake known as Alresford Pond. The project failed, however, as the "swallow holes" in the chalk allowed the water to leak away through the soil. The local effect, however, was important, as it caused houses to be built on the eastern side of the Alre, and thus New Alresford, the present town, developed.

It was during the eighteenth century, however, that practically all the important canals of our country were planned, and various canal schemes carried out in Hampshire, the chief objects being to link up the waterways, or to connect towns with the coast. Thus the Loddon and Wey canal was cut from Basingstoke to the Wey and Thames, and a scheme for canalisation of the Test from Southampton to Romsey and Andover was undertaken. This was never completed, but part of the channel from Southampton was later used for the L. and S.W. Railway. The Loddon and Wey canal is now derelict except for some local traffic from Aldershot and Frimley.

Water carriage, though slow, is cheap, and at one time it seemed that a great future existed for canals. The advent of railways in the early half of the nineteenth century, however, caused canals to decline. It is still a debated point whether with motor-engines canals cannot be usefully revived, but no Hampshire canal, except as above noted, is in use at the present time.

The real development of communication of modern days has been by the railway. In Hampshire we have the L. and S.W. Railway connecting Southampton, Winchester, and Portsmouth with London and the west of England; the Great Western linking it through Basingstoke with the Midlands; and certain other lines, viz., the Midland and S.W. Junction and the London Brighton and South Coast Railway—the former linking Southampton via Andover with the Midland Railway system, and the latter connecting Portsmouth with London and Brighton. In connection with the railway systems, the Isle of Wight is joined by steamer lines both with Portsmouth and Southampton.

The L. and S.W. Railway was opened in 1840, and others followed. The effect of the railways has been to revolutionise the conditions of the country. Towns off the railway, such as Odiham and Kingsclere, have declined or remained stationary, while elsewhere rapid development has been brought about. It is the modern railway that has made the modern large town possible. Since railways started, Southampton has developed very rapidly, and the combinations of dock and railway development have reacted each on the other, and made modern Southampton. Further, as we have already seen, it is at the "nodal points," or points of junction, that towns grow up. Railway development has intensified this, and led, as previously stated, to the growth of Basingstoke and Eastleigh, as well as in a lesser degree to Andover.

23. Administration and Divisions

By the time England had been consolidated into one kingdom under Egbert, the tun-ships, of which we spoke in Chapter I., had developed into manors, each with its own manor court or "tun moot," and the manors grouped into "hundreds." Each manor court met at first for the punishment of offenders, and the regulation of national defence, but later for other purposes, such as the "Trinoda Necessitas," namely the settling of military service, the repair of fortresses, and the upkeep of bridges. Later, when the Danegeld was imposed, money payments as well as payments by service were made, in addition to which there were tithes for ecclesiastical purposes. As time went on the tendency was more and more toward payments in money and, by the time of the Conquest, lands were assessed practically by fees paid by the knights, who held them—"Knight's fees" they were called—and the Domesday survey was in reality a survey of the land for purposes of exact assessment.

The next step came from ecclesiastical impulse. From the beginning of Christianity in Hampshire (A.D. 634), grants were made for Church purposes, and churches erected. These were intended at first for the benefit of the manorial lord himself and his people; and hence we often find the parish churches in the Squire's park—as at Warnford, Dean, and Avington. Regular dues, called tithes, were instituted, and ultimately districts were formed, comprising single manors or groups of manors, called parishes, the tithes of which were definitely appropriated to the support of a parish priest.

The parish, thus originally a purely ecclesiastical unit, later became the unit for local life also ; and when by Tudor days the system of cultivation in common had broken down, the manorial basis of local life began to break down also, and the parish took its place, though in many parts of the country the manor is still largely the unit for legal purposes. Parish church officials, such as churchwardens and parish clerks, came into existence, and the churchyard became the spot where parish and other meetings, social gatherings, and even fairs were held. Later, the parish meetings were held in the church vestry, and so the modern " Vestry-meeting " took its rise. To this day, though the Church as such takes little part in local government, lists of voters, ratepayers, and assessments are still affixed to the doors of churches. The development of the parishes was, however, a slow process and some of them did not come into effective existence till long after the Norman Conquest.

A further change took place in parish matters dating from about the thirteenth century. By this time the monasteries had gained possession of many manors and with them the corresponding tithes, and one of their number was appointed to carry out the parochial duties. These men were called " vicars " (*i.e.* deputies) and the monasteries themselves became the " rectors " (*i.e.* receivers of tithe). When in Henry VIII.'s reign the monasteries were dissolved, the tithe as well as the monastic estates in many cases came into private hands. In Hampshire most of them fell to Wriothesley, Earl of Southampton. Thus in many parishes to-day

The Town Hall, Portsmouth

the rector is a layman and the tithe is paid to him, while the parish priest is called the vicar, and receives only a small portion called the "smaller tithe." A further illustration of this point is that the care of the chancel of a parish church is always vested in the rector, whether clerical or lay, and he is personally responsible for its repair and upkeep.

With the increase of population, towns grew and became strong enough to exact special privileges for themselves, and to readjust or shake off the burdens which they had up till then borne. One form of duty levied on manors was the so-called "firma noctis unius," or maintenance of the king's household for one day in the year. Thus in Hampshire, in Edward the Confessor's time, Basingstoke, Kingsclere, and Hurstbourne were responsible for this amount between them, while Ellingham was charged with half one day's maintenance. The privileges just alluded to, which were usually conferred by charter, were generally the appointment of their own magistrates, and the raising of their own taxes—the right, in fact, of local self-government. In this way municipalities or boroughs came into existence—Winchester and Southampton in Henry II.'s reign, and Basingstoke in the thirteenth century. Andover, Alton, Odiham, and Portsmouth, as being royal manors, obtained various liberties from the king. Whitchurch, Fareham, and Alresford gained similar privileges from the bishop, and Romsey from the abbess of the convent there, and Lymington, Petersfield, and Christchurch were granted their liberties by the lords of their respective manors. In the fourteenth century Southampton added to its privileges extensive Admiralty rights over the whole Hampshire coast.

Areas over which these special privileges existed

were in general called "liberties," and were not confined to boroughs only. Thus the portion of Winchester outside the city, and therefore not under the authority of the mayor or bailiff, was a liberty, known as The Soke.

Great convents like Beaulieu and St Swithun's, Winchester, claimed and exercised extensive rights of sanctuary. In the latter a small manor, known as "Godbiete," granted by Queen Emma, Cnut's widow, to the prior and convent, was a "liberty" so complete that not even the king's warrant could be executed within it. Such sanctuaries became a nuisance and a danger, as every felon could find shelter in them.

The general government of the county was conducted in early days by Justices of the Peace—a title dating from the time of Edward III., though the actual office goes back to much earlier days—and their work was narrowly scrutinised by a Committee of Privy Council known as the Star Chamber. These justices met at Quarter Sessions, where not only was justice administered, but matters of county administration determined. But the needs of local government outgrew this machinery, and in 1888 a new era commenced, with the creation of elective councils for local purposes. Two classes of these were created, the larger districts became "County Boroughs," and the remainder of the county was divided into Administrative Counties under County Councils. Thus in mainland Hampshire we now have for general purposes the Administrative County of Southampton, and the three county boroughs, Portsmouth, Southampton, and Bournemouth. For certain purposes, the County Council exercises authority over the smaller boroughs—for other purposes they are quite independent. The County Government Acts of 1888 were in 1894 extended by the creation of Urban District Councils for minor urban areas, Rural District Councils for less populous areas, and Parish Councils for parishes.

For Poor Law purposes the county is divided into areas called Unions, and each Union is administered by a Board of Guardians. Hence the familiar term "Union," as the popular name for the poorhouse, or Union workhouse.

For Parliamentary purposes the county is divided into boroughs and county divisions. Bournemouth has one member, Southampton two, and Portsmouth three. The county divisions, apart from the Isle of Wight, are the Aldershot, Basingstoke, Fareham, New Forest, Petersfield, and Winchester Divisions. The Isle of Wight has a single member. In all this medley of areas and authorities, however, the ancient meaning of the county as a unit for organisation of defence and the administration of justice has not passed away. The ancient ruler of the county, the Ealdorman, still exists as the Lord Lieutenant, and by a recent act the organisation of matters relative to County Territorial Forces is placed under him. The ancient legal officer, the Shire-reeve, *scire-gerefa,* or Sheriff, still retains his title and office, and is responsible for the holding of the Assizes, and the carrying out of sentences.

In fact, local administration in English counties still follows the ancient lines—areas of administration and taxation go together; areas govern themselves, and elect their own responsible rulers, who exercise their rule in accordance with and under the supervision of the national government. A host of county and local officials, Lords Lieutenants, Chairmen of County Councils, Sheriffs, Mayors, Chairmen of Urban District Councils, of Parish Councils, of Rural District Councils, Boards of Guardians, and Justices of the Peace, all carry out responsible and often onerous duties, sometimes compulsorily, and all of them are unpaid for the work they do.

24. Roll of Honour

The worthies of Hampshire, as might be expected, form a long list. Great historic names, such as kings and bishops of Saxon and Norman times, we shall not refer to here. Of later state personages, Henry III. and Arthur, Prince of Wales, were born at Winchester, and William of Wykeham (1324–1404), the great builder and chancellor of Edward III.'s and Richard II.'s reign, was, as his name indicates, a native of Wickham near Bishop's Waltham. As Chancellor under Edward III., architect of the Round Tower of Windsor Castle, founder of New College, Oxford, and of Winchester, the first great public school of the country, as well as the great builder who gave Winchester Cathedral its present form, he calls for particular mention. He lived in Hampshire practically all his life, and died at his Palace, Bishop's Waltham, the ruins of which may still be seen.

Among great Hampshire families we may mention the De Ports of early Norman days, the Brocas family of Beaurepaire, whose Chantry Chapel at Sherborne St John is of much interest, the Tichbornes, the Paulets of Basing, the Basings of Stratton, the Montagus of Beaulieu, and later the Portals of Laverstoke. The Tichbornes have been in occupation of Tichborne from before the Conquest. Sir Benjamin Tichborne, the first baronet, figured prominently as Sheriff of the county in James I.'s reign. In more modern times the Tichborne family came prominently into public notice in consequence of the fraudulent attempt of an Australian butcher named Arthur Orton to claim the estate as the missing Sir Roger Tichborne, supposed to have been lost at sea, which resulted in the longest trial ever known in England, lasting from May 1871 to March 1872. William Paulet, Lord Treasurer in four reigns —Henry VIII., Edward VI., Mary, and Elizabeth —was a great statesman of his time, and high in Elizabeth's esteem. He lies buried in Basing Church. His descendant, "the heroic marquis," gallantly defended Basing House during its famous three years' siege.

The Cromwell family was identified with Hampshire. Richard Cromwell had estates at Hursley, and here for a considerable time he lived. He is buried in Hursley church, where a monument records his family and descendants.

The Lisles lived at Moyles' Court near Ellingham. Colonel Lisle was for a time Master of St Cross, Winchester. The tragedy of Dame Alicia Lisle's death has already been referred to.

The great statesmen of more recent days include the Duke of Wellington, whose seat, Stratfieldsaye, was presented to him by the nation; Lord Palmerston (1784–1865), born at Broadlands, near Romsey; and Earl Northbrook, sometime Viceroy of India, who carried out important work locally as Chairman of the Hants County Council.

Among great naturalists, Gilbert White of Selborne (1720–93) will always rank as the father of that school of careful and methodical observers who are the pioneers of exact knowledge and therefore of science. It has been truly said of him that "he ascertained more of the habits of the wild creatures of this country than any one man before or since." He was, moreover, the first to recognise and describe the harvest mouse and the great bat (*Pipistrellus noctula*). His letters on the *Natural History of Selborne,* which first appeared in 1789, are a leading classic. At Selborne, where he was born, he lived practically all his life, and lies buried in the churchyard on the north side of the chancel. Goodyear of Buriton, who died about 1658, is an early Hampshire naturalist, whose name deserves to be rescued from oblivion. William Curtis, of Alton, author of the *Flora Londinensis,* and founder of the celebrated *Botanical Magazine,* the introducer of many agricultural grasses, and of sea-kale as a vegetable, was a botanist of high merit. He died in 1799, but is still a famous name at Alton, where another member of the same name and family founded an Institute and Museum

Izaak Walton

in 1839. Another ardent naturalist was William Gilpin, rector of Boldre (1724–1804), the author of *Forest Sketches,* the Gilbert White, so to speak, of the New Forest, but he was even better known perhaps as a topographical artist and illustrator of books. His sketches, sold at his death, served to endow the parish school at Boldre. Izaak Walton (1593–1683) has every right to appear in our list of Hampshire worthies. He lived in Winchester after the death of his second wife, repeatedly fishing in the Hampshire

Charles Kingsley

streams, which he so warmly praises in his immortal book, the *Compleat Angler*, which was first published in 1653. Walton died at Winchester, and is buried in the cathedral. Charles Kingsley, the naturalist and writer, though not a native, was for thirty-one years Rector of Eversley, and closely associated with our county.

Of those who have won distinction in literature Hampshire is rich in names. William Lilye, born at Odiham in 1468, author of the *Brevissima Institutio*, better known as *Lilye's Grammar*, lived long at Rhodes

Hursley Vicarage

(*John Keble, Charlotte Yonge, and Dr Moberley in the foreground*)

and Rome. He was the earliest teacher of Greek in London, and became in 1518 the first master of St Paul's School. George Wither, a poet of unequal powers, mainly excelling in pastoral themes, was born in 1588 at Bentworth, and was much connected with the Puritans. He died impoverished in 1667, and is little read now, but Edward Young (1681–1765), author of *Night Thoughts*, who was born at Upham, still remains a well-known name.

Born on December 16th, 1775, at Steventon Rectory, and living nearly her whole life there and at Chawton till she moved to Winchester to die in 1817, Jane Austen is essentially Hampshire. Her novels deal with simple English domestic life, and aim neither at high romance nor sensation ; but for acuteness of perception and charm they command widespread admiration, and the lapse of a hundred years still leaves her one of the great English novelists. Charlotte Yonge, who was born at Otterbourne in 1823, and lived there practically all her life, a most prolific writer of novels for young ladies of the mid-Victorian period, commanded as large, if hardly as critical a public, and was a strong supporter of high-church tenets. Yet another well-known name among literary women of the county is Mary Russell Mitford, born at Alresford in 1789. Her scenes of country life and manners, collected in *Our Village*, will always live as a faithful and charming presentment of this subject long after her tragedies have been forgotten.

In a suburb of Portsmouth on February 7th, 1812, Charles Dickens was born, but his father left for London when he was an infant, and the county can do little more than claim the great novelist by right of birth. Another writer of renown born at Portsmouth is George Meredith (1828–1909). He began life as a journalist, and it was some time before he obtained full recognition of his powers as a novel-writer. Lack of naturalness in style and over-elaboration may restrict his readers, but cannot invalidate his position as one of the best novelists of his century. Ten years after his birth a third, and most deservedly popular novelist was born at Portsmouth. This was Sir Walter Besant, whose literary partnership with James Rice, editor of *Once a Week,* was as eminently happy as their novels. Charles Dibdin (1745–1814), the writer of the well-known song "Tom Bowling," might claim mention not less as a water-colour painter and dramatist than as a composer of songs, of which he wrote over 1300 in his lifetime. He was born at Southampton. Hampshire artists are not numerous. Vicat Cole, R.A., painter of sunny Surrey landscapes, was born at Portsmouth in 1833 and died in 1893.

Hampshire is identified in a remarkable degree with hymn writers. Thomas Sternhold (1500–49) author with Hopkins of the *Metrical Version of the Psalms,* was a Hursley man, and at that place he is buried. Thomas Ken, though not a Hampshire man by birth, was educated at Winchester, was Prebendary of the Cathedral, and wrote his *Evening* and *Morning Hymns,* and his *Manual of Prayer* for the use of Winchester boys. He won the esteem of King Charles II. by refusing to countenance his irregular life. As Bishop of Bath and Wells, he was later one of the "Seven Bishops." He died in 1711. Isaac Watts, of Huguenot descent on his mother's side, was born in 1674 at Southampton. Here he wrote "When I survey the wondrous Cross." He is perhaps the greatest of our hymn writers. "O God our help in ages past," "There is a land of pure delight" and other wonderful hymns are his. He died in 1748.

Memorial to Florence Nightingale
(*In the Crypt of St Paul's Cathedral*)

John Keble, the leader of the Oxford Movement, a Gloucestershire man by birth, was for thirty years resident in the county, first as curate, and later as rector of Hursley, but the *Christian Year* was written in 1827, some time before he took the living. Thomas

Whiting, Master of the Querister's School at Winchester College, wrote the fine hymn for those at sea—"Eternal Father," and Henry Twells, of Bournemouth, was the author of many hymns of distinction.

Another name which will always rank high on the Hampshire list of worthies is that of Florence Nightingale, the heroine of Scutari, the "Lady of the Lamp," a native of East Wellow. The beautiful memorial of her by Frederick Walker here given is in the Crypt of St Paul's Cathedral.

25. The Chief Towns and Villages of Hampshire

Aldershot (35,175), grew after Crimean War from a small village to a large military town. Barracks arranged in three lines—Wellington, Stanhope, and Marlborough. The camp is about 7 square miles in extent. (pp. 10, 80, 126, 164, 171.)

Alresford, New (1706), ancient market town, conterminous with **Old Alresford,** 7 m. N.E. of Winchester. Bishop Godfrey de Lucy (1189-1204) made a great dam between the two Alresfords, forming Alresford Pond (23 acres), to improve the navigation of the Itchen. Churchyard has tombstones of French prisoners, who died here during the Napoleonic Wars. A tablet marks Miss Mitford's house in Broad Street. Rodney's tomb is in Old Alresford church. (pp. 29, 85, 98, 121, 126, 151, 164, 169, 178.)

Alton (5555), market town, extending 1 m. along London road. Centre of Hants hop trade. Fine 15th cent. church, with chancel of 13th cent., and good Jacobean pulpit. Scene of fight in Civil War in 1643, when Col. Boles was killed in the church itself. There are fairs for sheep and cattle on last Saturday in April and on September 29. Grammar School founded 1638. (pp. 97, 98, 104, 105, 119, 121, 124, 126, 134, 141, 151, 169, 174.)

Alverstoke. Parish includes Gosport and Rat Island, the Haslar and New Barracks, and the Royal Marine Barracks.

Andover (7596), ancient borough on River Anton, at meeting of a number of roads. Present church, nearly all

Broad Street, Alresford

modern, has a fine Norman doorway. Two important Roman roads—the Portway and that from Winchester to Cirencester—crossed near here, and the neighbourhood is full of antiquities, Roman and Saxon—the Devil's Ditch, Bury Hill, Danebury Hill, etc. The Grammar School was founded in 1569. (pp. 23, 81, 103, 105, 121, 126, 130, 158, 159, 164, 165, 169.)

Ashley (88), 7 m. W. of Winchester, has a Norman and E.E. church with Norman font and chancel arches. Traces of a Roman camp in neighbourhood. (pp. 81, 134.)

Avington (231), ½ m. from Itchen Abbas Station. Avington House, often visited by Charles II., is the seat of the Shelley family. In the park is the ancient "Gospel Oak." The 18th cent. church has state pews of mahogany. (pp. 109, 166,)

Baddesley, North (280), 3 m. S.S.E. of Romsey. The small but ancient church of St John Baptist has a chained Bible. Jacobean pulpit, and tomb of a knight of St John of Jerusalem. Rectory stands on site of commandery of the Knights of St John.

Barton Stacey (542), 5 m. S.E. of Andover, adjoins Bransbury Common. E.E. church with fine Perp. tower. 166.) (pp. 85, 143, 145, 159.)

Basing, Old (1353), 2 m. N.E. of Basingstoke, the site of a battle between the Danes and English in 871. Fine Perp. church, with two chantry chapels, and monuments. Near here are the ruins of Basing House, the ancient seat of the Paulet family, and the scene of the historic siege. (pp. 86, 124, 126, 131, 143, 145, 149, 173.)

Basingstoke (11,540), busy railway and agricultural centre and manufacturing town at fork of main roads from London to Salisbury and Winchester. It has agricultural implement works, clothing factories, and large motor and engine works. Fine late Perp. church. Near station is ancient cemetery known as the Litten (Saxon *lictun* = corpse enclosure), with ruins of chapel of the Holy Ghost. (pp. 32, 85, 100, 102, 105, 141, 143, 145, 150, 151, 164, 165, 169, 171.)

Beaulieu (986), at head of estuary of Beaulieu River. Here are extensive and very interesting ruins of Cistercian Abbey, Beaulieu, the refectory of which is now the parish church. Two miles down the river is Buckler's Hard, formerly a naval shipbuilding yard. (pp. 50, 57, 60, 65, 86, 106, 108, 110, 123, 146, 150, 170, 173.)

Bedhampton (775), close to Havant. Great springs here supply Portsmouth waterworks. There is a Norman chancel arch in St Thomas's church, and a fine old yew in the churchyard. (p. 31.)

Bentley (671), 6 miles N.E. of Alton, on L. & S.W.R. St Mary's church has a late Norman font, and 15th cent. clerestory windows in the chancel. (pp. 41, 97.)

Bighton (200), 2 m. N.E. of New Alresford, Norman and E.E. church with Norman font.

Binsted (1376), on Wey, 4 m. N.N.E. of Alton. In centre of hop country. The church of St Cross is of the 12th century, with good Knight Templar monument. (p. 43.)

Bishopstoke (2191), on the Itchen, now merged in Eastleigh U.D. (pp. 80, 104.)

Bishop's Sutton (200), on Pilgrim's Way, between Alresford and Alton. The Bishops of Winchester formerly had a residence here. St Nicholas church has very small Norman nave windows, and two good Norman doorways.

Bishop's Waltham (2488), 10 m. S.E. of Winchester. Formerly a seat of the Bishops of Winchester, shows ruins of the palace built by Bishop Henry of Blois. William of Wykeham died here (1404), and Margaret of Anjou, wife of Henry VI. An artificial lake, the Abbot's Pond, forms the head of the Hamble River. (p. 173.)

Bitterne (3142) (the Roman Clausentum), faces Southampton on opposite side of Itchen estuary. (p. 134.)

Boarhunt (492), 3 m. N.E. of Fareham. Late Saxon church, with exterior pilaster-strips, and Saxon font and window. On Portsdown Ridge is the Nelson monument, a prominent landmark, erected in 1814.

Boldre (2504), New Forest village, 2½ m. N.W. of Lymington. The church of St John has much Norman work, including an arcade of three arches. William Gilpin, artist and author of the *Forest Scenery*, was vicar for thirty years, and is buried here. (p. 175.)

Botley (1012), on Hamble Creek. Centre of the early strawberry culture. William Cobbett lived here. (pp. 85, 95.)

Bournemouth (78,674), a modern health-resort and winter residence on Poole Bay, has attained its present size from quite modest dimensions during the last half-century. Its pine-woods, for which it is famous, are said to contain three million trees, all of recent introduction, and of various species. There are various hospitals and sanatoria for phthisical patients. **Boscombe** is a large and increasing suburb. (pp. 4, 9, 38, 49, 50, 56, 60, 64, 80, 110, 171, 181.)

Bramley (417), 5 m. N.E. of Basingstoke. Highly interesting Norman and later church, with tombs of the Brocas family, and remains of 13th cent. frescoes of the murder of Thomas à Becket.

Bramshott (2453), village 1 m. N. of Liphook. Longmoor Camp, recently established, has caused a rapid growth of population. The church is mainly E.E. The beautiful artificial ponds known as Wakener's Wells, and other relics of ancient ironworks, are close by. (pp. 11, 106.)

Breamore (505), on the Avon, 2½ m. N.N.E. of Fordingbridge, is of peculiar interest. The church dates from Anglo-Saxon times; there are external pilaster-strips, a Saxon chancel arch, and Crucifixion group over the S. porch. An ancient maze near is a relic of Breamore Priory, founded 1132. Breamore House, a partly Elizabethan structure, adjoins. (pp. 10, 138.)

Brockenhurst (2048), 4 m. from Lyndhurst, in the New Forest. St Nicholas church is partly pre-Conquest, with square Norman font and ancient yew in churchyard. (pp. 86, 140.)

Broughton (872), on the Roman road from Winchester to Sarum, has a Trans. Norman, and E.E. church, St Mary's.

Burghclere (542), (one of the three Hampshire "cleres"—Kingsclere held by the King, Highclere by the Bishop, and Burghclere by a Baron), 4 m. S. of Newbury, on G.W.R. Beacon Hill, Ladle Hill, and the Seven Barrows are local antiquities. (pp. 86, 130, 141.)

Buriton (771), 2 m. S. of Petersfield, at foot of Butser Hill. St Mary's church has a Norman nave. (p. 11.)

Bursledon (1018), 4½ m. S.E. of Southampton, on Hamble Creek. There is some shipbuilding and coasting trade, and strawberry culture. (pp. 101, 134.)

Candover — three villages — Brown Candover (178), Chilton Candover (103), Preston Candover (407), lying N. of Alresford, in Candover Valley. Fine avenue, half a mile in length, of ancient yews, near Chilton Candover. (pp. 29, 48, 81.)

Catherington (1663), 5 m. N. of Havant. All Saints is an Early Norman church, with fine tower, and Hyde and Napier monuments.

Chawton (714), 1½ m. S.W. of Alton, the home of Jane Austen for the last eight years of her life. Chawton House is of Elizabethan date.

Cheriton (690), 6 m. S.E. of Winchester, near source of the Itchen, which flows through it in a number of channels, crossed by bridges. Fine E.E. church. Local traditions survive of the battle of Cheriton, fought here in 1644. (p. 29.)

Chilcomb (182), adjoins Winchester, and has church of the time of the Norman Conquest.

Christchurch (5104), borough at junction of Avon and Stour, at head of Christchurch Harbour. Has a magnificent priory church, the remains of Christchurch Priory, built

Christchurch Priory

by Flambard, showing beautiful Norman and E.E. work, and very perfect vaulted Perp. choir with canopied stalls. There are also several fine chantry and other chapels, a splendid reredos of Perp. period, and a monument to the poet Shelley under the W. tower. There are also ruins of Christchurch Castle, and of Norman domestic buildings. (pp. 9, 30, 55, 57, 60, 62, 81, 82, 107, 120, 140, 143, 146, 147, 149, 151, 169.)

Church Oakley (214), 4½ m. S.W. of Basingstoke, at head of Test valley, has an interesting flint church dedicated to St Leonard, rebuilt 1500. Malshanger, in the neighbourhood, was the birthplace of Archbishop Wareham, and the ancient seat of that family.

Clatford, Upper (654), has a mill and ironworks. Its interesting church has a two-arched arcade dividing nave and chancel. **Goodworth Clatford** (436), St Peter's church has early Norman and Trans. nave and shingled spire. (pp. 84, 142.)

Compton (767), 2½ m. S. of Winchester. All Saints church has Saxon windows, and Norman nave and font. On Compton Down Cromwell encamped at the opening of the siege of Winchester. There are some barrows in the neighbourhood.

Corhampton (115), in Meon Valley. Has an ancient Saxon church with "Frith Stone," and a very fine old yew. (pp. 81, 137.)

Cosham (2528), a large village on the mainland opposite Portsea Island, formed by the amalgamation of the parishes of Widley and Wymering. (pp. 57, 151.)

Crawley (502), a village 4 m. N.W. of Winchester, much of which has recently been rebuilt in picturesque style. St Mary's church is chiefly E.E., with traces of an earlier Norman building. (p. 85.)

Crondall (1374), a large village 4 m. N.W. of Farnham. All Saints church is Trans. Norman, and has some interesting brasses. At Barley Pound is a camp, near which a Roman pavement and other remains were found; and "Caesar's Camp," to the S.E., is an earthwork of great strength. (pp. 44, 142.)

Corhampton Church, Meon Valley

(*Showing Anglo-Saxon Work*)

Crookham (2739), 3 m. S.W. of Fleet, is now the centre of the Hampshire tobacco industry. (p. 98.)

Curdridge (805), 1 m. E. of Botley. In centre of strawberry area. William Cobbett formerly lived here, at Fairthorne Manor.

Damerham (549), 2½ m. N.W. of Fordingbridge, was transferred from Wiltshire to Hampshire in 1895. (p. 11.)

Dibden (=Deep-dene), 1 m. W. of Hythe. Formerly a "purlieu," *i.e.*, freed from the Forest Law. The

Roman road can be traced from here to Stone Point. Church E.E. (pp. 66, 86, 158.)

Droxford (655), village on Meon, 5 m. E. of Bishop's Waltham. Norman church, with E.E. nave arcades, and some much later work, restored 1847. (pp. 85, 104, 134, 140.)

Dummer (276), 5 m. S.W. of Basingstoke. All Saints church dates from 13th century, has a curious baldacchino-like structure, which formerly covered the rood, some interesting brasses, and a wooden belfry.

Eastleigh (15,247), large modern industrial centre at junction of Portsmouth and Southampton lines, L. & S.W.R. Carriage and locomotive works employ the bulk of the workmen. (pp. 30, 100, 102, 165.)

Easton (375), attractive village, with picturesque thatched cottages, on the Itchen, 3 m. N.E. of Winchester. St Mary's is a fine late Norman and E.E. church. (pp. 87, 141.)

Eling (3125), at head of Southampton Water, on the edge of the New Forest, has an early Norman church, St Mary's, restored 1865. The parish embraces Totton, where are large flour and wood-sawing mills. (p. 86.)

Ellingham (225), 3 m. N. of Ringwood, on Avon. All Saints, now called St Mary's church, is largely of 17th century date. Dame Alice Lisle's tomb is near S. wall of nave. Moyles Court is 1 m. from the village. (pp. 86, 126, 169, 174.)

Empshott (167), a small village, 6 m. S.E. of Alton, has an interesting E.E. church (Holy Rood), with a curious glazed belfry, and a good screen and font. (p. 43.)

Emsworth (2224 in 1901), included in Warblington, 2 m. S.E. of Havant, on Chichester Harbour. It is a yachting station, with fishing and coasting trade. The place is celebrated for its oyster beds. (pp. 108.)

Eversley (841), 5½ m. N. of Winchfield, on the border. Charles Kingsley, curate and rector here from 1842 to 1875, is buried in the churchyard. Bramshill, a fine Jacobean residence built in 1607 for Prince Henry, son of James I., is near. (pp. 109, 176.)

Fareham (9674), market town and small port at N.W. end of Portsmouth Harbour. Busy industrial centre, with tanyard, flour mills, and potteries, and an active coasting trade. (pp. 57, 104, 105, 134, 169, 171.)

Farley Chamberlayne, a small parish 7 m. S.W. of Winchester, with a church containing the monuments of the St John family for some three centuries.

Farnborough (14,199), near Aldershot. An important military and air-craft centre. Parts of the parish church are Norman, and there is a beautiful wooden porch of the 15th century. The Roman Catholic memorial church contains the mausoleum of Napoleon III. and the Prince Imperial. (pp. 9, 80, 126.)

Farringdon (428), 3 m. S. of Alton. Church E.E. Gilbert White was curate here, 1761-1785.

Fawley (2033), scattered village on Southampton Water, 3 m. N.W. of Calshot, with fine Norman and E.E. church (All Saints). (p. 140.)

Fleet (3281), residential town on Basingstoke line, some 3 m. west of Farnborough. Fleet Pond, about ¾ m. in length, and 130 acres in extent, is the largest lake in the county.

Fordingbridge (3456), on Avon, 10 m. S. of Salisbury. Ancient New Forest town, formerly with busy manufactures. Has an E.E. and Dec. church (St Mary), with carved wood roof. (pp. 9, 30, 110, 130, 138.)

Gosport (33,300) (= God's port), in Alverstoke Parish, on W. side of Portsmouth Harbour. Important seaport, and naval victualling centre, with harbour, naval hospital, and large barracks. There are some interesting Georgian houses. H.M.S. *Victory*, Nelson's flagship, lies on the Gosport side of Portsmouth Harbour. Handel's organ is in the church of the Holy Trinity. (pp. 80, 100.)

Grateley (266), 7 m. S.W. of Andover. The church is noticeable as possessing some E.E. stained glass, formerly in Salisbury Cathedral. (p. 84.)

Greatham (1772), 5 m. N.E. of Petersfield, is now rapidly developing, owing to the establishment of Bordon and Longmoor Camps close by. (p. 43.)

Greywell (246), (locally pronounced Grewell), 5 m. E. of Basingstoke. The church of St Mary has a wooden tower, a remarkable carved rood-loft, and a pre-Conquest chancel.

Hambledon (2139), a straggling village 7 m. S.E. of Bishop's Waltham, with Georgian houses fronting street. Early home of English cricket, with historic matches played on Broadhalfpenny Down. The Bat and Ball inn was formerly kept by Richard Nyren, the great Hambledon cricketer. The Church of SS. Peter and Paul has a good deal of Norman and E.E. work. (p. 31.)

Hamble (695), at mouth of Hamble Estuary. Centre of shell-fish industry, much of it being imported. The training ship *Mercury*, where boys are prepared for the navy, lies up the river. The church of St Andrew has a Norman doorway. (pp. 57, 62, 95, 101, 107, 108, 134.)

Havant (4092), market town, at the head of Langston Harbour. The church of St Faith is partly Norman, and contains a beautiful E.E. window. (p. 110.)

Hayling Island (2309), 4 m. by 1½ m.; an increasingly popular sea-side resort in Langston Harbour. S. Hayling church of St Mary the Virgin has a very fine yew tree, and a Norman font recovered from the sea. The seashore, which has very fine sands, has suffered greatly from erosion. (pp. 11, 48, 50, 51, 65, 85.)

Headbourne Worthy (240), 1½ m. N. of Winchester. St Swithun's church has Saxon remains, including a defaced Saxon rood on the western wall. (pp. 24, 30, 139.)

Headley (7576), extensive parish, 4½ m. N. of Liphook. Population rapidly increasing owing to establishment of Bordon military camp.

Highclere (428), 4½ m. S.W. of Newbury. Highclere Castle, with magnificent park, residence of the Earls of Carnarvon, is 2 m. distant. (p. 86.)

Highcliffe (1638), favourite sea-side place, 2½ m. from Christchurch. Considerable erosion on coast, threatening Highcliffe Castle. (p. 64.)

Holybourne (565), on the Wey, 1 m. N.E. from Alton. The church of the Holy Rood is E.E., with a Norman tower.

Hordle (1065), on Christchurch Bay. Hurst Castle, in this parish, 3 m. distant, at the end of a narrow promontory, is a fortress guarding the Western entrance of the Solent, originally built in Henry VIII.'s reign. Charles I. was imprisoned here about seven weeks before his execution. (pp. 60, 62, 117, 123, 125, 149.)

Hound (3478), ½ m. from Netley. Small, but interesting E.E. church (St Mary), with fine yew in churchyard. The ruins of Netley Abbey—founded in 1237 by Henry III., and belonging to the Cistercians — are of considerable extent.

Hursley (940), 5 m. S.W. of Winchester. John Keble, curate and afterwards vicar here (1835 to 1866), rebuilt the church out of the profits of the *Christian Year*. He is buried in the churchyard, and Richard Cromwell in the old church, where are monuments of Cromwell family, and of Sternhold, the metrical psalmist. (pp. 173, 179, 180.)

Hurstbourne Priors (389), on the Test, 3½ m. N.E. of Andover. St Andrew's church has Norman doorway. Hurstbourne Park is the seat of the Earls of Portsmouth. (pp. 27, 81, 131, 140, 155, 169.)

Hurstbourne Tarrant (719), 5 m. N. of Andover. St Peter's church has Trans. Norman doorway, and a spire with shingle roof. (pp. 28, 145.)

Itchen Abbas (232), 4 m. N.E. of Winchester, on Itchen, has a church with Norman chancel and doorway. An offshoot of St Mary's Abbey, Winchester.

King's Somborne (1263), interesting water village on the Somborne, 3 m. S. of Stockbridge, with thatched, daub-wall cottages and a flint church of Dec. period.

Kingsclere (2475), small town, 8 m. N.W. of Basingstoke, has a Norman church dedicated to St Mary, with monuments to the Kingsmill family. The Kingsclere racing stables are famous. (pp. 36, 86, 142, 169.)

Laverstoke and Freefolk (389), united parishes on Test, 3 m. E. of Whitchurch. Laverstoke House, seat of the Huguenot family of Portal, who have made bank-note paper since 1724. Freefolk Chapel, built 1265, was authorised by a Bull of Pope Clement. (pp. 27, 79, 84, 85, 104, 173.)

Liss (2334), a large village, 4 m. N.E. of Petersfield, rapidly growing owing to military camps in neighbourhood. (pp. 43, 52.)

Littleton (218), 3 m. N.W. of Winchester. The small church, dedicated to St Catherine, is mainly Norman.

High Street, Lymington

Longparish (729), on the Test, 4 m. E. of Andover. "Deadman's Plack," in the neighbouring Harewood Forest, records the murder of Earl Æthelwold by King Edgar.

Longstock (413), on the Test, 5 m. S. of Andover. Interesting village, with many old thatched cottages. A Danish dock for long ships has been recently found here. (p. 78.)

Lymington (4329), borough and market town on estuary of Lymington River, with ferry to the Isle of Wight. Has a mayor and corporation. Formerly engaged in the salt industry, is now a yachting and minor shipbuilding centre. (pp. 50, 57, 62, 65, 106, 110, 169.)

Lyndhurst (2406), a small town in the New Forest, having a fine modern church with a Leighton fresco. Courts of Swainmote are held here, and there are interesting Forest relics. (p. 49.)

Meon-East (1013), in Meon Valley, 4 m. W. of Petersfield. All Saints church is a Norman and E.E. building, with a remarkable black stone font. (See under **St Mary Bourne.**) (pp. 140, 144.)

Meon Stoke (458), adjoins Corhampton and Exton in Meon Valley, at foot of Old Winchester Hill, on which is the site of a Roman camp. (p. 130.)

Meon-West (799), picturesque village on the Meon, 3 m. W. of East Meon, with a church (St John the Evangelist) of squared flints, mainly of Dec. period. (p. 30, 77.)

Micheldever (997), on L. & S.W.R., 7 m. N. of Winchester. The church is modern and of peculiar style, with an octagonal nave. The tower is all that remains of the ancient church, which was destroyed by fire. (pp. 81, 145, 159.)

Milford-on-Sea (1618), an attractive and rising summer resort on Christchurch Bay. The E.E. (and partly Norman) church of All Saints has a quaint tower. The cliffs hereabouts abound in fossils. (pp. 56, 64.)

Minstead (892), an attractive New Forest village, 2 m. N.N.W. of Lyndhurst, has an interesting Norman and E.E. church. The Rufus Stone, at the N.W. part of the parish, is supposed to mark the spot where William Rufus was killed. (p. 85.)

Mottisfont (559), 4½ m. N.N.W. of Romsey, is on the Test. Mottisfont Abbey stands on the site of an Augustinian Priory of the 12th cent., of which portions remain. There is a fine Norman chancel arch in St Andrew's church. (p. 28.)

Nately Scures (355), 4 m. N.E. of Basingstoke, has an exquisite little 12th cent. Norman church (St Swithun's). (p. 141.)

Netley (see **Hound**), 6 m. S.E. of Southampton, is renowned for its naval hospital and the ruins of the Cistercian Abbey. (pp. 62, 108, 123, 146.)

Newnham (577), 4½ m. N.E. of Basingstoke. There is a Norman chancel arch in the church of St Nicholas.

Nursling (661), on the Test, 3½ m. S.E. of Romsey, has an interesting E.E. church (St Boniface), with monuments. Winfrid, afterwards St Boniface, the evangelist of Germany, was educated in the monastery here at the end of the 7th century. (p. 158.)

Odiham (2674) (*i.e.* Woodyham), a picturesque market town, lies off the railway, 3 m. S.W. of Winchfield station, and was a royal residence of the kings of Wessex. There is a fine E.E. church, and ruins of a Norman castle. The endowed Grammar School was founded in 1694. The stocks and whipping-post are still preserved. (pp. 86, 120, 126, 147, 149, 169, 177.)

Otterbourne (1012), on the Itchen, 4 m. S.W. of Winchester. Here Charlotte Yonge, the novelist, lived many years, and Keble was vicar. (pp. 30, 158, 178.)

Overton (1616), at the head of the Test Valley, 8 m. W. of Basingstoke. St Mary's is an early church of mixed styles, with a massive modern tower. Overton is famous for the large sheep fair held here July 18th. (pp. 27, 81.)

Owslebury (pronounced Usslebury, from "Ouse"= water) (819), is a village standing high, 5 m. S.S.E. of Winchester. Marwell Hall, in part early 14th century, and Fisher's Pond, are near. (p. 81.)

Petersfield (4329), ancient town at the head of the Rother. Market place has equestrian statue of William III. St Peter's church has a very fine Norman chancel arch and some E.E. windows. Fine scenery of South Downs, with Butser Hill and other high points near, and a lake of 22 acres. Has a large cattle and sheep fair on October 6th. (pp. 11, 24, 33, 41, 43, 72, 126, 132, 151, 169, 171.)

Market Day, Petersfield

Portchester (901), a Roman sea fortress, much of the ruins of which still remain, covering 9 acres. In Norman days was the chief war port; now superseded by Portsmouth, and left high and dry. Fine ruins of Norman castle. The fine Norman church of St Mary was originally the church of an abbey built by Henry II., and removed later to Southwick. At the end of the 18th cent. many French prisoners of war were interned at Portchester and, later, Dutch prisoners taken at the battle of Camperdown. (pp. 51, 76, 82, 110, 111, 120, 132, 134, 140, 147, 149, 157.)

Portsmouth (231,144), large town, naval station and arsenal, and seaport, 74 m. S.W. of London, Consists of four parts, Portsmouth being the garrison town, Portsea the dockyard, Landport the workers' town, and Southsea the watering-place. It is the most important naval station in the world, and is very strongly fortified. It has a long and interesting history, receiving its first Charter from Richard I. Villiers, Duke of Buckingham, was murdered here 1638. St Thomas's church, the Garrison church, the Dockyard, Gun Wharf, Sally Port, and famous old hotels are among the chief objects of interest. The house where Charles Dickens was born is now the Dickens Museum. (pp. 4, 8, 31, 50, 57, 60, 62, 72, 80, 100, 107, 110, 112, 117, 122, 124, 125, 127, 145, 161, 165, 170, 171, 178, 179.)

Redbridge (=Reedbridge), in Millbrook parish, at mouth of the Test, 4 m. N.W. of Southampton, with reed swamps all along the estuary. It has some shipping trade. (pp. 62, 85.)

Ringwood (5055), market town on the Avon, 8 m. N. of Christchurch, on western edge of New Forest. An industrial centre, chiefly making gloves and agricultural implements, and celebrated for its ale. (pp. 30, 85, 103, 110, 126.)

Rockbourne (447), on western edge of county, 3½ m. N.W. of Fordingbridge. The church of St Andrew has a Norman doorway and wooden tower. A Roman villa was found here in 1913.

Romsey (4669), very ancient borough and market town on the Test, 7 m. N.W. of Southampton. Romsey Abbey is the church of the ancient abbey, originally founded here 910; it dates from Norman days, and is a particularly good example of a conventual church. Outside the S. transept is a beautiful Saxon rood. Romsey was given its charter by James I., and is a busy little town, with tannery, several mills, and a factory of Berthon collapsible boats. Paper milling, once extensively carried on here, has now almost ceased. A bronze statue by Noble of Palmerston, who was born at Broadlands, in the neighbourhood, stands in the market place. (pp. 28, 40, 105, 109, 110, 119, 123, 125, 139, 140, 146, 150, 164, 169, 174.)

Ropley (1371), a large parish, containing many scattered hamlets, some 4 m. E. of Alresford.

Sarisbury and Swanwick, an ecclesiastical parish formed out of Titchfield in 1837, is a great centre for the early strawberry industry. (p. 86.)

St Mary Bourne (1152), on the Bourne, 5 m. N.E. of Andover. St Peter's is an interesting Trans. Norman church, with a black stone font of Tournai marble, similar to that of East Meon church, and of which there are four examples in the county, the others being at Winchester Cathedral and St Michael's, Southampton. The church contains a Crusader's tomb. (p. 144.)

Selborne (2118), 4½ m. S.E. of Alton. Immortalised as the home of Gilbert White. The churchyard has a famous yew tree. The Wakes, where Gilbert White lived, the Plaistowe (=play spot), and the Hanger, are the chief points worthy of note. The country all round is extremely interesting and full of charm. (pp. 22, 41, 43, 48, 52, 97, 153, 161, 174.)

Sherborne, Monks (494), 3½ m. N.W. of Basingstoke. A fine E.E. chancel, part of the old Priory church, and elegant Norman tower, formerly central, remain.

Sherborne St John (627), 2 m. N. of Basingstoke. The interesting church of St Andrew has chained books, brasses of the Brocas family, and a good Jacobean pulpit. A mile N.E. is a fine Elizabethan mansion, The Vyne, the home originally of the Sandys family. Beaurepaire, the home of the ancient family of Brocas, is also in the parish. (p. 173.)

Sholing (4746), near Woolston, is practically a suburb of Southampton.

Silchester (423), 8 m. N.N.W. of Basingstoke. Walls of Roman city of Calleva are still standing. The whole site, of 100 acres or more, has been recently carefully excavated, and the objects discovered have been placed in the Reading Museum. The church of St Mary is Norman and E.E., and has a good chancel screen. (pp. 76, 82, 84, 117, 132, 133, 134, 156, 157, 158.)

Soberton (1302), is a large village on the Meon, 4½ m. E. of Bishop's Waltham. St Peter's church is partly E.E. and Dec., and has a lofty western tower. (p. 145.)

Sopley (819), on Avon, 2 m. N. of Christchurch. St Michael's church is mainly E.E., with tower bearing a short spire. Tyrrel's Ford and Smithy (the latter now closed) preserve the tradition of Sir Walter Tyrrel and the death of Rufus.

Southampton (119,012), a borough, great commercial port and mail-steamer station, with extensive docks and shipbuilding yards, already described, still has much of historic interest, such as the curious Bargate, the ancient walls and city gates, and the Domus Dei Hospital of the 13th cent., with its French Protestant church. St Michael's church has a Norman tower, and an early black stone font. Southampton is the headquarters of the Ordnance Survey, where ordnance maps are printed. In the neighbourhood, about 2 m. to the S.E., are the ruins of Netley Abbey, and the Royal Victoria Hospital just beyond. Southampton industries are numerous, but for the most part of a maritime nature. (pp. 3, 4, 6, 10, 26, 30, 50, 62, 66, 76, 100, 101, 102, 104, 105, 112, 115, 117, 120, 122, 127, 134, 141, 144, 147, 148, 157, 158, 164, 165, 169, 170, 171, 179.)

Steventon (229), 6 m. S.W. of Basingstoke. Jane Austen was born here in 1775. (p. 178.)

Stockbridge (915), a long, straggling market town on the Test, 8½ m. N.W. of Winchester, between Danebury and Woolbury Rings. It is famous for trout fishing and eels, and has an annual sheep fair on July 10th. The famous Danebury Stables are about 3 miles away. It was at Stockbridge that Robert of Gloucester was taken prisoner, while engaged in a rearguard action to permit of the escape of his sister, the Empress Maud, from Winchester to Ludgershall and Devizes. (pp. 110, 130.)

Stoke Charity (121), 7 m. N. of Winchester. Has some historic monuments in the very interesting Norman church of St Michael.

Stoneham, North and **South** (1962 and 1934). Two villages lying N. by E. of Southampton. The former has an interesting church (St Nicolas), with the tomb of Lord Hawke, and another to some Venetian sailors who died while on a voyage to Southampton in medieval times.

Stratfieldsaye (460), 8 miles N.E. of Basingstoke, on the Berks border. Includes the estate and house presented to the Duke of Wellington by the nation after Waterloo. Here is the Wellington Monument designed by Baron Marochetti (pp. 82, 174.)

Sydmonton (146), 1 m. E. of Burghclere. St Mary's church has a good Norman doorway removed from the original church. (pp. 33, 84, 140.)

Tadley (1293), a scattered parish, 6 miles N.W. of Basingstoke. St Peter's is a small E.E. church with a good carved pulpit, dated 1650.

Tidworth, South (4840), about 6 m. N.W. of Andover, has large military barracks. North Tidworth is in Wilts. (pp. 10, 80, 84, 126, 130.)

Thruxton (654), 5 m. W. of Andover. Roman antiquities are abundant in neighbourhood. The church (S.S. Peter and Paul) is chiefly Dec. and Perp., and has some fine early monuments. (p. 84.)

Tichborne (=Itchen Bourne), (286), a charming, old-world village, 2 m. S.W. of Alresford, on the Upper Itchen Valley. Seat of the Tichborne family from before the Conquest. Has a Norman church (St Andrew's) of great interest, with ancient pews and pulpit, and monuments of the Tichbornes. (pp. 29, 86, 140, 173.)

Titchfield (1608), small but ancient town near mouth of Meon. Here formerly stood a Premonstratensian Abbey, pulled down by Wriothesley, Earl of Southampton, Chancellor to Henry VIII., who built Place House, ruins of which remain. The church is of great interest, with Norman work, decorated chantry chapel, and a monument to Wriothesley. Here Charles I. embarked for the Isle of Wight when attempting to escape from the Roundheads. (pp. 31, 125, 146.)

Twyford (2048), a beautiful village, 3 m. S. of Winchester, on the Itchen. Pope was at school here, and here Benjamin Franklin wrote most of his autobiography. In the churchyard is an ancient clipped yew. Large Sarsen stones are numerous. (pp. 30, 44, 48, 87.)

Upham (622), 3 m. N.N.W. of Bishop's Waltham. Young, the author of the *Night Thoughts*, was born here, 1684.

Wallop, Nether (701), **Over** (543), and **Middle** (hamlet), on the Wallop Beck, 4 to 5 m. W. and N.W. of Stockbridge. On Danebury Hill is an early circular earthwork. (pp. 10, 130.)

Warblington (3771), is a large village on the Sussex border, 1 m. S.E. of Havant. The ancient church of St

Thomas à Becket is very interesting, and has some Saxon work. Some ruins of the castle exist. (pp. 140, 158.)

Warnford (**Warrenford**) (176), a small village on the Meon, 6 m. N.E. of Bishop's Waltham. King John's House, a ruin in Warnford Park, is a misnomer derived from the St John family, to whom it once belonged. Warnford was the scene of Wilfrid of York's evangelising of the Meon Valley, as recorded by ancient stone tablets in the church, which has a Norman tower, an E.E. nave, and a Saxon sundial. (pp. 142, 166.)

Weeke or Wyke (108), adjoins Winchester. The ancient church contains a curious brass of 1498, with a figure of St Christopher. (p. 85.)

Wellow, East (393), **West** (646), scattered parishes some 4 m. W. of Romsey, on the border. Florence Nightingale is buried in E. Wellow Churchyard. (pp. 12, 181.)

Weyhill, in Penton Grafton parish (377), 3 m. W.N.W. of Andover, is noted for its great stock and agricultural produce fair held here annually, October 10th-14th. The chancel in the church (St Michael) is of early Norman date. (pp. 121, 155.)

Wherwell (529) (locally pronounced Horrell), a historic village on the Test, 4 m. S.E. of Andover, near Harewood Forest. Of the famous abbey, built here by Elfrida, widow of King Edgar, no traces now remain. (pp. 27, 28, 84, 119, 146, 159.)

Whitchurch (2370), a small but ancient town on Test, with a mayor but no corporation. It has mills and a fishing centre, with memories of Kingsley. All Saints church has a curious effigy in stone of Frithburga, a Saxon lady. (pp. 27, 109.)

Winchester from St Giles' Hill

Reredos, Winchester Cathedral
(*Erected by Bishop Fox*)

Wickham (1198), village 4 m. N. of Fareham, on the Meon, with a pleasing market square. Was the birthplace of William of Wykeham, in 1324. (p. 85.)

Winchester (23,378), a city, forming county town and ancient capital of England, known to the Britons as Caer Gwent, to the Romans as Venta Belgarum, and to the Saxons as Wintan-ceastir, and full of historic memories of early kings of Wessex, Egbert, Alfred, Cnut, William the Conqueror, etc. Of ancient fortifications, Westgate and Kingsgate and some portions of the walls remain. The Cathedral, begun in 1079, the County Hall, the ruins of

"School," Winchester College
(*The great School Room built by Warden Nicholas*, 1683)

Wolvesey Palace, and Hyde Abbey are all of special interest, as is Winchester College, the mother of English public schools, founded here by William of Wykeham, in 1387. Winchester is an assize city, and the headquarters of County Council of the Administrative County of Southampton. The beautiful Norman hospital of St Cross, 1 m. to the S., was founded in 1132. (pp. 29, 36, 38, 55, 76, 82, 99, 103, 105, 108, 117, 118, 119, 120, 121, 124, 125. 126, 130,

132, 134, 140, 143, 146, 147, 148, 149, 156, 157, 158, 159, 161, 165, 169, 170, 171, 172, 176, 178, 179, 180.)

Winchfield (466), 9 m. E. of Basingstoke, on L. & S.W.R. There is much Norman architecture in St Mary's church, notably a narrow Norman chancel archway, and a beautifully carved and moulded W. door. (pp. 85, 140.)

Wolverton (166), 5 m. N. of Oakley. The beautiful red brick church of St Catherine is said to have been designed by Sir Christopher Wren.

Wonston (=Wonsington), (856), on the Bullington Stream, 6 m. N. of Winchester. The S. doorway of the church (Holy Trinity), is Norman.

Woodhay, East (1642), a scattered parish in the Enborne Valley. The Bishops of Winchester formerly had a palace here. West Woodhay is in Berks. (p. 86.)

Woolston (1341), a suburb of Southampton on E. side of Itchen estuary, opposite Southampton Docks. Is an extensive shipbuilding centre, Thorneycroft's motor-boat works employing many hands. (pp. 30, 80, 101.)

Yately (1879), on the Blackwater, on the N.E. border of the county. St Peter's church is mainly E.E., but has a Norman N. doorway.

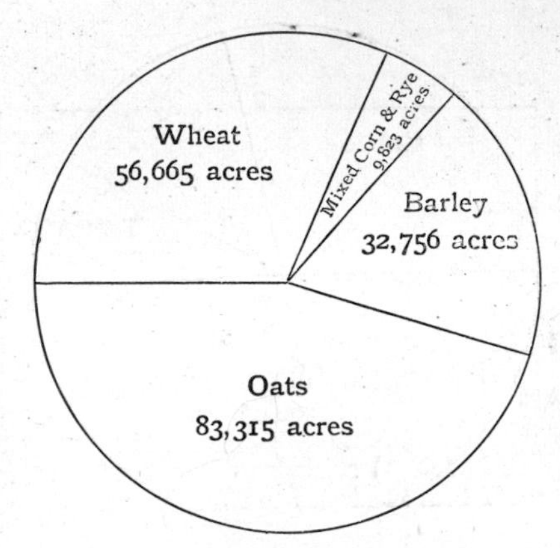

Fig. 5. Proportionate areas of chief Cereals in Hampshire in 1920

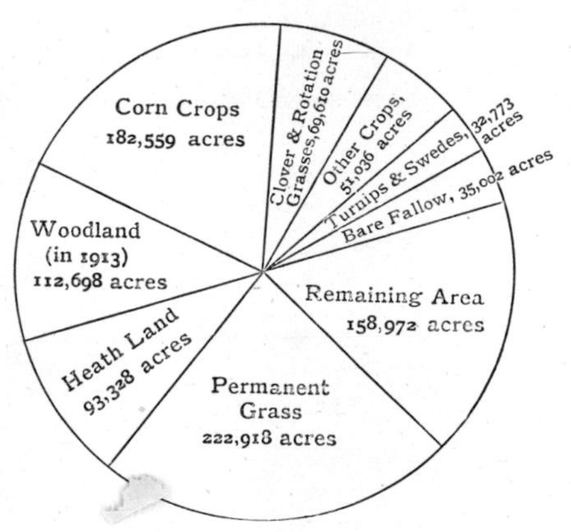

Fig. 6. Proportionate areas of Land in Hampshire in 1920

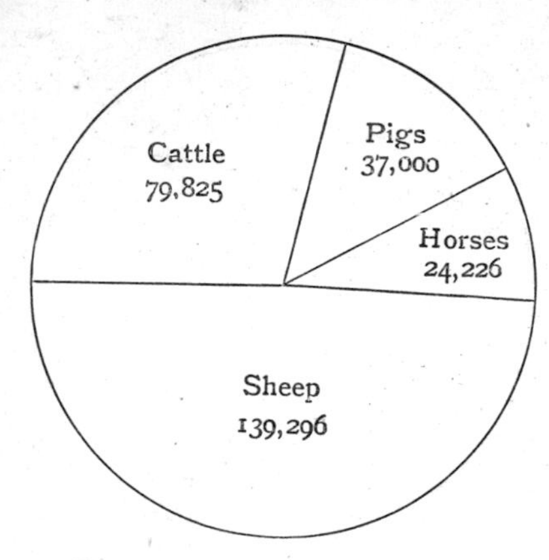

Fig. 7. Proportionate numbers of Live Stock in Hampshire in 1920

ENGLISH CHANNEL
The Solent
Spithead
NEW FOREST
ISLE OF WIGHT
Southampton Water
Christchurch B.
Selsea Bill
Fordingbridge
Ringwood
Lyndhurst
Bradley Plain
Lymington
Milford
Keyhaven
Hurst Castle
Christchurch
Bournemouth
Hengisbury Hd.
Beaulieu
Walhampton
Lower Exbury
Calshot Cas.
Southampton
Bishops Waltham
Fareham
Titchfield
Hook
Gosport
Portsmouth
Southsea
Havant
Bere Forest
Emsworth Sta.
Westbourne
Rowlands Castle Sta.
Chichester
Thorney I.
Chichester Harbour
Cowes
E. Cowes
Osborne
Kings Quay
Fishbourne Cr.
Binsted
RYDE
Nettlestone Pt.
Brading Har.
Bembridge Pt.
Foreland
White Cliffe B.
Culver Cliff
Sandown
Sandown Bay
Shanklin
Dunnose
Luccomb Chine
Bonchurch
Ventnor
St. Catherine's Pt.
Knowle
Blackgang Chine
Walpon Chine
Chale B.
Whale Chine
Cowleaze Chine
Barnes Chine
Brixton B.
Grange Chine
Chitton Chine
Brook Chine
Compton B.
Freshwater B.
Scratchells B.
The Needles
Allum B.
Totlands B.
Yarmouth
Newtown
NEWPORT
Godshill
Mottistone
50'
40'
30'
20'
10'
1° W. of Greenwich
The Cambridge University Press
Copyright. George Philip & Son Ltd.

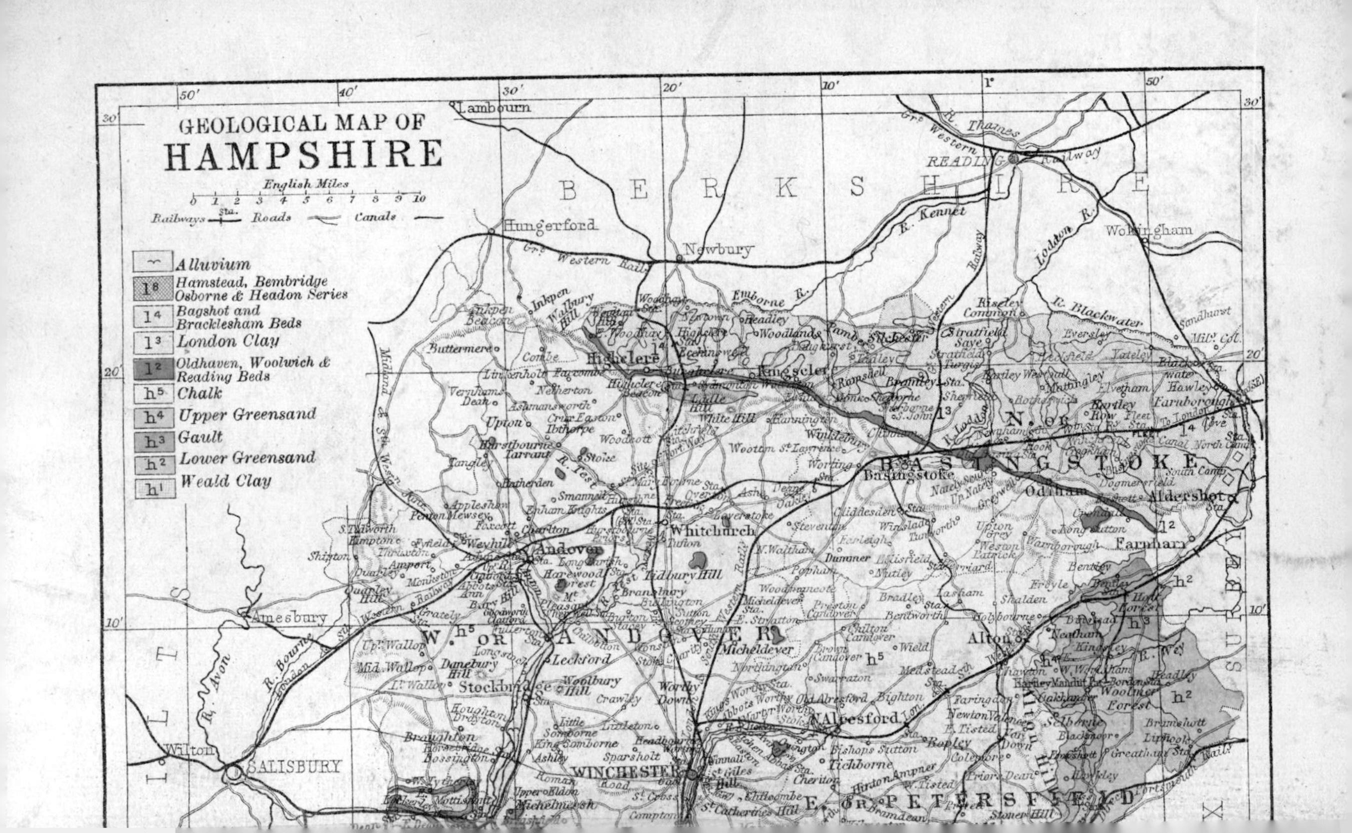
GEOLOGICAL MAP OF
HAMPSHIRE
English Miles
0 1 2 3 4 5 6 7 8 9 10
Railways Sta. Roads Canals
Alluvium
1⁸ Hamstead, Bembridge Osborne & Headon Series
1⁴ Bagshot and Bracklesham Beds
1³ London Clay
1² Oldhaven, Woolwich & Reading Beds
h⁵ Chalk
h⁴ Upper Greensand
h³ Gault
h² Lower Greensand
h¹ Weald Clay
BERKSHIRE
SURREY
Lambourn
Hungerford
Newbury
READING
Wokingham
Highclere
Kingsclere
Andover
Whitchurch
BASINGSTOKE
Basingstoke
Odiham
Aldershot
Farnham
Alton
Alresford
Micheldever
Stockbridge
WINCHESTER
Amesbury
SALISBURY
Wilton
W. OR ANDOVER
N. OR BASINGSTOKE
E. OR PETERSFIELD